SD329
Science: Level 3

The Open University

Signals and perception:
the science of the senses

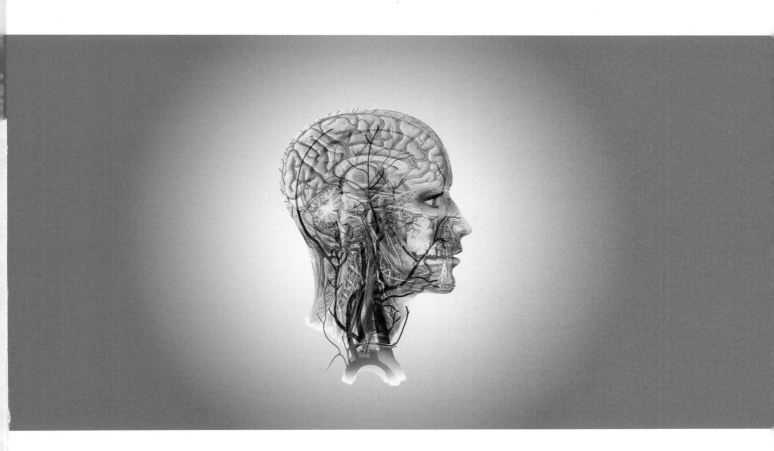

Block 1 Introduction to the Senses
Block 2 The Sensory Nervous System

This publication forms part of an Open University course SD329 *Signals and Perception: the science of the senses*. The complete list of texts which make up this course can be found at the back (where applicable). Details of this and other Open University courses can be obtained from the Student Registration and Enquiry Service, The Open University, PO Box 197, Milton Keynes MK7 6BJ, United Kingdom: tel. +44 (0)845 300 60 90, email general-enquiries@open.ac.uk

Alternatively, you may visit the Open University website at http://www.open.ac.uk where you can learn more about the wide range of courses and packs offered at all levels by The Open University.

To purchase a selection of Open University course materials visit http://www.ouw.co.uk, or contact Open University Worldwide, Walton Hall, Milton Keynes MK7 6AA, United Kingdom for a brochure. tel. +44 (0)1908 858793; fax +44 (0)1908 858787; email ouw-customer-services@open.ac.uk

The Open University
Walton Hall, Milton Keynes
MK7 6AA

First published 2002. Second edition 2005. Reprinted 2008.

Edited and designed and typeset by The Open University.

Printed and bound in the United Kingdom at the University Press, Cambridge.

ISBN 0 7492 1450 3

2.2

The SD329 Course Team

Course Team Chair
David Roberts

Course Manager
Yvonne Ashmore

Course Team Assistant
Margaret Careford

Authors
Mandy Dyson (Block 3)
Jim Iley (Block 6)
Heather McLannahan (Blocks 2, 4 and 5)
Michael Mortimer (Block 2)
Peter Naish (Blocks 4 and 7)
Elizabeth Parvin (Blocks 3 and 4)
David Roberts (Block 1)

Editors
Gilly Riley
Val Russell
Sue Betteridge

Indexer
Jean Macqueen

OU Graphic Design
Roger Courthold
Jenny Nockles
Andrew Whitehead

CD-ROM and Website Production
Jane Bromley
Eleanor Crabb
Patrina Law
Kaye Mitchell
Brian Richardson
Gary Tucknott

Library
Judy Thomas

Picture Research
Lydia Eaton

External Course Assessors
Professor George Mather (University of Sussex)
Professor John Mellerio (University of Westminster)

Consultants
Michael Greville-Harris (Block 4, University of Birmingham)
Krish Singh (Block 2, Aston University)

BBC
Jenny Walker
Nicola Birtwhistle
Julie Laing
Jane Roberts

Reader Authors
Jonathan Ashmore (University College London)
David Baguley (Addenbrooke's Hospital, Cambridge)
Stanley Bolanowski (Syracuse University)
James Bowmaker (University College London)
Peter Cahusac (University of Stirling)
Christopher Darwin (University of Sussex)
Andrew Derrington (University of Nottingham)
Robert Fettiplace (University of Wisconsin)
David Furness (Keele University)
Michael Greville-Harris (University of Birmingham)
Carole Hackney (Keele University)
Debbie Hall (Institute of Hearing Research, Nottingham)
Anya Hurlbert (University of Newcastle upon Tyne)
Tim Jacob (University of Cardiff)
Tyler Lorig (Washington and Lee University)
Ian Lyon (Consultant)

Don McFerran (Essex County Hospital)

Keith Meek (University of Cardiff)

Tim Meese (Aston University)

Julian Millar (Queen Mary, University of London)

Peter Naish (Open University)

Robin Orchardson (University of Glasgow)

Alan Palmer (Institute of Hearing Research, Nottingham)

Krish Singh (Aston University)

Charles Spence (University of Oxford)

Rollin Stott (DERA Centre for Human Sciences)

Steve Van Toller (University of Warwick)

Stephen Westland (University of Derby)

INTRODUCTION TO THE SENSES

Contents

1

Experiencing the world

Concerning the thoughts of man, … they are every one a representation or appearance of some quality, or other accident of a body without us, which is commonly called an object. Which object worketh on the eyes, ears, and other parts of man's body, and by diversity of working produceth diversity of appearances. The original of them all is that which we call sense, (for there is no conception in a man's mind which hath not at first, totally or by parts, been begotten upon the organs of sense) …

Leviathan, Thomas Hobbes (1588–1679)

1.1 Introduction

Philosophers from the time of the ancient Greeks to the present day have puzzled over the way in which we interact with our environment. It was realized at a very early stage, even before the time of Thomas Hobbes, that we obtain all our experience and knowledge of the world through our senses.

○ How many human senses do you think there are?

● Most people would say five: vision, hearing, touch, smell and taste. However, there are several others such as the sense of balance, pain, pressure, temperature, position, and movement. These are often (incorrectly) grouped under 'touch', and comprise what is known as the somatic sensory system.

Most of us take our senses for granted. It is only when we damage or lose the use of one or more that we realize how much we depend on them.

Look at Figure 1.1. It is a photograph of a flock of the very beautiful bird called the roseate spoonbill (*Ajaia ajaja*). You can gain some appreciation of their beauty through looking at the picture. But this restricts you to a single sense, vision. On the

Figure 1.1 A flock of roseate spoonbills at the Ding Darling National Wildlife Area, Sanibel Island, Florida.

other hand, the photographer when taking the picture was aware of other sensations: the sounds, not just of the spoonbills but of other wildlife too, and the characteristic smell of a late afternoon on a sunny March day in southern Florida. He was also conscious of the ambient temperature and of his sense of balance while taking the photograph. All these combined to create a memorable sensory experience. For those who were present when it was taken, looking at the photograph evokes that memory, but for those who were not, viewing the image, though beautiful, is only a one-dimensional experience.

Imagine then the effect of experiencing total lack of sensation. In practice, total sensory deprivation is difficult to achieve. However, if the sensory inputs experienced by adults normally used to the full range of sensation are eliminated or severely reduced, the brain begins to compensate in a variety of ways. Being reduced to drawing solely on internal sources for perceptual experience, the effect is to hallucinate, to begin to experience the loss of one's identity, to feel apathetic and to suffer severe depression. Research subjects exposed to a total sensory deprivation environment can typically only tolerate the experience for a maximum of about four days. It is hardly surprising, then, that sensory deprivation has been widely used as a method of torture for prisoners in many parts of the world. The effects that lack of adequate sensory stimulation may produce are also of major concern for astronauts who undertake extended space flights.

The effect of sensory deprivation on young children is far worse. It is known that sensory stimulation plays an absolutely crucial role in both the physical growth and organization of the brain in young animals. Studies of children in the first years of life who have been dreadfully neglected and have suffered extensive sensory deprivation (some unfortunates being literally kept in cages in dark rooms) have been found to exhibit permanent effects as shown in Figure 1.2. In the CT scan on the left is an image from a healthy three-year-old with an average head size. The image on the right is of a three-year-old child suffering from severe sensory-deprivation neglect. This child's brain is significantly smaller than average and has abnormal development of the brain area known as the cerebral cortex. It is possible that a number of factors could contribute to these observations, lack of proper nutrition being a key one. However, by comparing the relative rate of growth of other organs compared to the growth of the brain, it is difficult to conclude otherwise than that these effects are the result of lack of sensory stimulation.

1.2 Human nervous system

Before we proceed any further, it is necessary to give a brief introduction to the human nervous system, that is what might, in computing terms, be called the hardware involved in sensation and perception. The obvious place to begin is the brain. The brain is composed of two main type of cell: **neurons** and **glial cells**.

Neurons are specialized cells. Their function is to receive, process and transmit information, and this is achieved by means of electrical signals. In the human body billions of neurons are connected together to form the nervous system. Virtually all neurons are present at birth. What happens as a child grows and develops is that the number and type of *interconnections* between neurons greatly increases. Sensory stimulation and experiences create more interconnections, and so without these the development of the brain is clearly stunted.

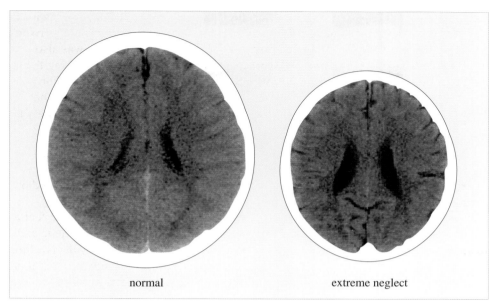

normal   extreme neglect

Figure 1.2   These images illustrate the impact of sensory deprivation on the developing brain. They have been obtained by the technique called computed tomography imaging, commonly abbreviated to CT or CAT (computed axial tomography) scan, now routinely used in hospitals to check for injuries or abnormalities such as tumours. You will learn more about CT and other imaging techniques later in the course. The CT scan on the left is an image from a healthy three-year-old child with an average head size. The image on the right is from a three-year-old child suffering from severe sensory-deprivation neglect. These images are from studies conducted by a team of researchers from the Child Trauma Academy led by Bruce D. Perry, MD PhD.

Glial cells greatly outnumber neurons, by a factor of around 10 in humans. Glial cells do not seem to be directly involved in information processing – this is a function reserved for neurons – but rather have a range of vital support roles. For example, during the development of the brain, certain types of glial cells guide the connections that are formed between neurons, and other types produce a fatty substance called myelin that acts as an insulator for neuronal axons, the 'wiring' of the nervous system that conducts the electrical signals.

The human nervous system consists of the brain, the spinal cord, and various peripheral nerves which are connected either to the spinal cord or directly to the brain (Figure 1.3, overleaf). The spinal cord is a continuation of the brainstem (see below) and is enclosed and protected by the vertebrae that make up the spine. The peripheral nerves are of two types: **afferent** nerves provide the information to the brain from the various sensory receptors, whereas **efferent** nerves carry instructions from the brain to muscles or as feedback information to modify the sensory input.

The brain lies within the cranial cavity of the skull. The appearance of the brain is dominated by the large pair of **cerebral hemispheres** that are folded over, hiding underlying structures (Figure 1.4a, overleaf). Each hemisphere is covered with a highly folded sheet of many interconnected neurons called the **cerebral cortex**. It is a sheet, about 3 mm thick, consisting of billions of interconnected neurons, and is highly folded to fit into the skull. The cerebral cortex, which is responsible for sensations, perceptions, learning, voluntary movement, speech and cognition, is the

Figure 1.3   The human nervous system.

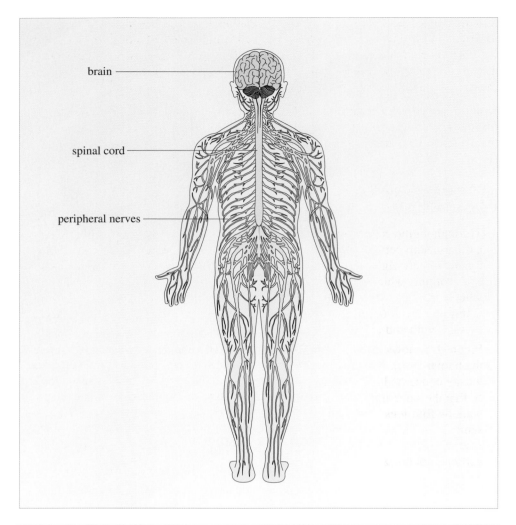

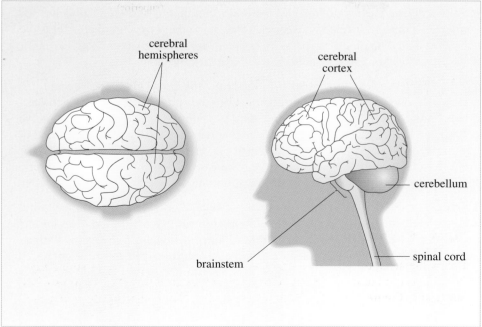

Figure 1.4   The human brain viewed from above and from the side.

least developed part of the brain at birth. Other distinctive structures that can be seen externally are the **brainstem**, **cerebellum** and **spinal cord** (Figure 1.4b). Externally, there are four main divisions, called lobes, visible within each cerebral hemisphere. These are named the **frontal**, **parietal**, **temporal** and **occipital lobes** according to their relationship to bones in the skull (Figure 1.5).

In addition to this brief introduction to the nervous system, it will help greatly throughout the course if you become familiar at this stage with some basic terms that describe the various spatial directions when discussing the nervous system (Box 1.1).

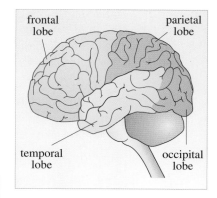

Figure 1.5   The four lobes of each cerebral hemisphere.

Box 1.1   Anatomical directions

Throughout the course, we shall often need to describe a particular direction or a relationship between two components of the sensory system. Using the terms up, down, left, right, over, under, in front, behind, etc. can often be ambiguous. For example, which eye is on the left and which on the right depends on whether you are looking at a person from the front or from the back. Consequently in order always to be clear about what is meant, we need to be familiar with and use the recognized anatomical terms.

Figure 1.6 shows the various directional terms that are used when describing the human body. Note that these have different meanings depending on whether we are concerned with the nervous system above or below the neck. This arises so that the same nomenclature can be used for all mammals. In mammals that walk on four legs, the orientation of the brain and the rest of the body is the same. In humans, and other mammals that walk upright, the brain retains essentially the same orientation with respect to the ground, but the body is vertical, not horizontal.

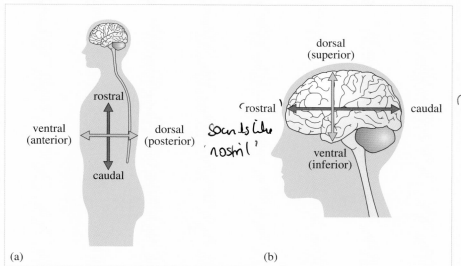

Figure 1.6   The anatomical directions (a) below and (b) above the neck.

Below the neck, the terms **dorsal** or **posterior** are used for what we normally think of as our backs, and **ventral** or **anterior** are used for what we think of as our fronts (Figure 1.6a). The term we use to describe the parts of the nervous system closer to the brain is **rostral** (meaning 'towards the nose'), and parts further from the brain are said to be **caudal** (meaning 'towards the tail').

Above the neck, dorsal, often used interchangeably with **superior**, means the top of the brain, and ventral, often taken to be synonymous with the term **inferior**, refers to the underneath of the brain. Rostral and caudal refer respectively to the front and rear of the brain (Figure 1.6b). Note that the alternatives to dorsal and ventral are different in the two situations.

The above terms differentiate the 'top' and 'bottom', and the 'front' and 'back'. There are also some terms that are used when considering the relationship between one side and the other. These are the same for all parts of the body, irrespective of whether they are above or below the neck. If a vertical plane is drawn that divides the body into left and right halves, then if a structure is closer to that plane it is said to be **medial**, and if further away it is **lateral** (Figure 1.7). If two structures are on the same side of the plane they are said to be **ipsilateral** to one another, and if on opposite sides, they are in a **contralateral** relationship.

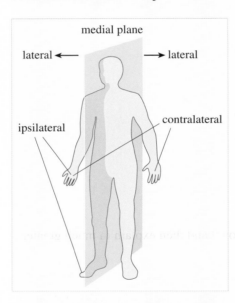

Figure 1.7   The lateral anatomical directions.

Two other terms that are often used are **proximal** and **distal**. They are used to specify the relationship to what can be regarded as the 'centre' or 'origin' and the 'periphery' or 'termination'. So, a structure that is proximal to another structure is a structure that is closer to the centre or origin and conversely distal means further from the centre or origin.

Finally, it is often useful to consider cross-sections through various parts of the body, particularly the brain. Cross-sections are usually taken in two vertical planes at right angles to each other and in the horizontal plane. Each of these has its own special name. The plane that divides the brain in half horizontally is called simply the **horizontal plane** (Figure 1.8a) as is any plane parallel to that. Each of the planes that divide any front section and back section of the brain is called the **coronal plane** (Figure 1.8b). The plane that divides the two cerebral hemispheres is called the **sagittal plane** (Figure 1.8c), with any plane parallel to that having the slightly different name of **parasagittal**.

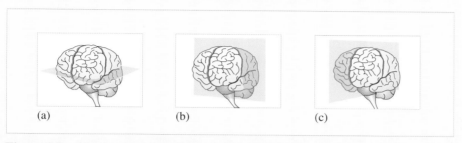

(a)   (b)   (c)

Figure 1.8   The three section planes: (a) horizontal; (b) coronal; (c) sagittal.

1.3 Sensation and perception

The process of **sensation** consists of two overlapping stages, reception of the signal and interpretation of the signal. The initial reception stage is the physical interaction with the environment. The resulting stimulation of the appropriate part of the nervous system causes a message to be sent to the brain, which then processes the information it receives, incorporating stored experiences, in the process called **perception**.

○   What are the signals for sight, hearing, touch and smell?

●   Sight requires light, hearing involves sound, touch requires pressure, and smell involves volatile molecules. You may not have known all these, but do not be concerned: we shall give a preliminary description of what is involved in each of the senses in Section 2 and then explain in much greater detail in subsequent blocks.

The study of the relationship between physical stimuli and the resulting perception is called **psychophysics**. Though it is often convenient to distinguish between the signal reception stage of sensation and the perception stage, with the latter encompassing the information processing function, as we shall see later it is not always easy to make a clear distinction. However, one of the best examples of the difference between sensation and perception is found in random dot autostereograms, which are 3D images. These pictures are known as **single image random dot stereograms (SIRDS)**, or **single image stereograms (SIS)** depending on whether the picture contains random dots as a base for the 3D effect, or a repetitive pattern. You may have seen these as posters or in books. At first sight, they look like multicoloured abstract patterns, but if you stare at them for long enough (from just a few seconds up to several minutes), eventually most people can see a three-dimensional image appear.

○ Why does this clearly demonstrate the difference between sensation and perception?

● The initial sensation of viewing the abstract image is clearly quite different from the final image that is perceived. During the time between starting to view the image and recognizing the 3D image embedded in it, the brain is processing the visual signals it is receiving as well as searching its memory banks to produce the final result.

Figure 1.9 shows an example of an SIS image. Follow the instructions given in the caption to view the 3D image. Do not be too concerned if you are unable to see the hidden image, as 10–15 per cent of the population cannot see these.

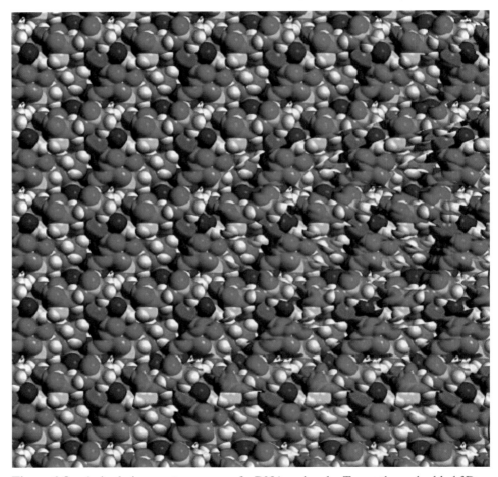

Figure 1.9 A single image stereogram of a DNA molecule. To see the embedded 3D image, you need to place the book vertically, allow your eyes to relax, and focus on a spot some distance *behind* the image you are looking at. The process depends on looking at a point further away than the image you are looking at but focusing on that image. Some people find this quite difficult for the first time. This 'decoupling' of your vision is contrary to what you normally do when looking at something, and is the main obstacle to seeing the 3D effect. One way of achieving this is to get really close to the image, so that your nose almost touches it. Let your eyes relax and stare into the distance. Move away from the image very slowly, keeping your eyes unfocused all the time. Eventually, the 3D image of the helical DNA molecule should just 'pop' out of the page.

Most people with fully functioning senses generally do not distinguish the two stages of sensation and perception. Normally, this only becomes apparent when we are confronted by unusual examples. The distinguished psychologist Ian Howard put this in a nutshell:

> Many people do not realize that perception is a problem; they perceive the world so effortlessly and continuously that they take the mechanism for granted. Perception is the most neglected of all the major problems of science, and this may be because it is the most difficult problem of them all.

I. P. Howard, *Human visual orientation*, John Wiley, New York, 1982, p. 1.

In fact, since that book was written much progress has been made in the understanding of perception by combining the tools of psychology with recently developed physiological techniques and imaging methods. None the less, it has proved much more difficult in general to provide explanations of the perception stage than of the initial stages involving stimulation of the receptors and the subsequent transmission of nerve impulses to the brain. We shall examine some of the unusual examples referred to above when we consider the phenomenon of illusions later in this block, but it is worth looking at one such example now. This example is called a **subjective contour**. Figure 1.10a shows four disks with cut-out sectors (looking rather like 'Pacman' figures). The disks are just seen as four individual units. In Figure 1.10b, however, where the orientation of the cut-out disks is different, the perception is of a white square appearing to lie over the top of four discs. This illusory square, known as a Kanizsa square, disappears if you cover up the disks.

While it is known that, in general, adults and older children have the ability to perceive such illusory figures, until recently little has been known about when and how infants develop this crucial skill. The main problem in finding out has been that at such a young age, children cannot tell you whether they see just the Pacman figures, or the illusory square as well. Scientists at Birkbeck College in London have recently been able to measure the electrical activity in the brains of infants using a geodesic sensor net, which comprises a group of 64 sensors held on the baby's scalp by a kind of hairnet (Figure 1.11).

Previous studies with adults had shown that viewing the four Pacman-like shapes oriented as in Figure 1.10b gave rise to a characteristic burst of brain activity involving large groups of nerve cells within the brain firing together in a particular rhythmical pattern, called 'gamma oscillations'. This is correlated with the perception of the illusory square. When viewing the arrangement shown in Figure 1.10a, the gamma oscillations are not detected. The Birkbeck scientists found identical results in a group of eight-month-old babies, indicating that they too had the ability to perceive the square. In contrast, when a group of six-month-old babies were shown the same pictures, the gamma oscillations were not present. This work indicates that not only do babies as young as eight months have the ability to recognise complex objects, but that the brain undergoes an important stage in development in the short period between six months and eight months.

We shall explore the perception stage of the various senses as we discuss them individually throughout the course. For now, we shall move on to take a preliminary look at each of the fully functioning senses in turn.

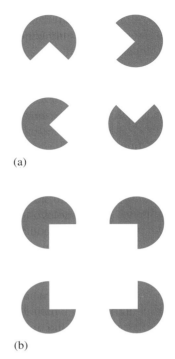

(a)

(b)

Figure 1.10   Diagrams illustrating (a) the absence and (b) the presence of a subjective contour known as a Kanizsa square.

Figure 1.11   The geodesic sensor net used to measure electrical activity in the brain.

1.4 Summary of Section 1

We gain all our experience of the external world through our senses. The development of the brain from birth onwards, particularly in the first years of life, depends on the information received from the senses. Extended sensory deprivation leads to permanent damage to the brain.

The brain is composed of two main types of cell: neurons and glial cells. Neurons are cells specialized for information processing and transmission. Glial cells, which greatly outnumber neurons, do not seem to be directly involved in information processing but have a range of vital support roles. In the human body billions of neurons are connected together to form the nervous system. Virtually all neurons are present at birth. It is the number and type of interconnections that greatly increases as a child grows and develops.

The human nervous system consists of the brain, the spinal cord, which is enclosed within the column of vertebrae that make up the spine, and various peripheral nerves, which are connected either to the spinal cord or directly to the brain. The peripheral nerves are of two types: afferent nerves provide the information to the brain from the various sensory receptors; efferent nerves carry instructions from the brain to muscles or provide feedback information to modify sensory input.

The appearance of the brain is dominated by the cerebral hemispheres. Each hemisphere is covered with a highly folded sheet of many interconnected neurons called the cerebral cortex, which is responsible for sensations, perceptions, learning, voluntary movement, speech and cognition. Other distinctive structures are the brainstem and cerebellum. Each cerebral hemisphere has four main divisions or lobes.

The process of sensation comprises two overlapping stages: reception of the signal and interpretation of the signal, called perception. A good example to show that the two stages are distinct is the perception of a 3D image when viewing a single image stereogram. Another example is the perception of a subjective contour (a Kanizsa square) by babies.

Question 1.1

Which of the following statements relating to human anatomy are true and which false? *[handwritten: lateral = towards outside / away from centre]*

(a) The nose is lateral to the left eye and medial to the right eye. *[handwritten: away from]*

(b) The cerebellum is caudal to the frontal lobe. *[handwritten: caudal = brain]*

(c) Each ear is contralateral to the other. *[handwritten: contralateral = opposite sides]*

(d) The parietal lobe is rostral to the temporal lobe. *[handwritten: towards front ? both near centre of brain]*

(e) The spinal cord lies in a rostral-caudal direction. *[handwritten: lot from brain]*

(f) The spinal cord is situated to the posterior of the medial plane. ✓

[handwritten margin notes: above the neck / rostral = front / caudal = back / dorsal / superior > above]

Question 1.2

Explain what you understand by the terms sensation and perception. *[handwritten: Physical signals from environment]* *[handwritten: what the brain makes of them]*

Question 1.3

The eye is often described as operating like a camera. Give two examples described in Section 1 that indicate that the sense of vision differs very significantly from photography.

[handwritten: Pacman / Kanizsa square + stereogram after-image]

Introducing our senses

2.1 Hearing

The sense of hearing plays many important roles in our lives. The ability to communicate with others through speech, particularly and increasingly by telephone, is central to everyday life. Hearing plays an important role in survival: even as simple an activity as crossing a road relies on our hearing to warn us of approaching traffic that we may be unable to see because of a bend or a parked vehicle obscuring the view. Beyond these utilitarian functions, there is the enjoyment of listening to music, which can elicit a wide range of emotions and memories. These are but a few examples of how we rely on our sense of hearing.

○ Recalling that the process of sensation consists of two overlapping stages, reception of the signal and perception, where are the receptors for hearing located?

● Nearly everyone would know that these are in the ear, though perhaps few would know exactly where in the ear the interaction takes place.

Figure 2.1 shows a cutaway diagram of the human ear. Sound enters mainly via the auditory canal, the passageway from the outer ear (**pinna**), and impinges on the eardrum (**tympanum**) located in the middle ear, causing it to vibrate. The vibrations are transmitted via a complex mechanism to the **cochlea** in the inner ear where the receptors are located, which is where the signal is transformed into electrical signals that are sent to the brain. Also located in the inner ear are the **semicircular canals** which are the organs of another sense, that of balance, and are the heart of what is called the vestibular sensory system. We shall not discuss this any further now, but you will learn about it in Block 3.

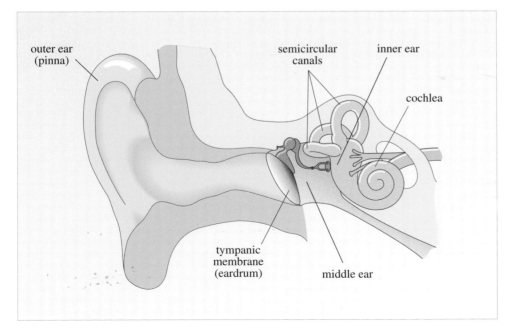

Figure 2.1   A cutaway diagram of the human ear.

Sound is produced by objects vibrating. The vibrations can be very unpleasant to listen to, such as those produced by a jet engine at full speed or an electric drill boring a hole, giving rise to what we call **noise**. On the other hand, the vibrations can be more pleasant, for example speech, birds singing, or a guitar string being plucked. For simplicity, we shall concentrate on those vibrations that are pleasant to listen to.

Sound is transmitted through the air because the vibrations give rise to periodic variations in pressure. If the frequency of the vibrations is in the range 20–20 000 Hz (Box 2.1), then the sounds are audible to humans. It is perhaps easiest to visualize this process in the case of a loudspeaker in a sound system or television. This operates by means of a cone to which is attached a magnet. The electrical signal induces the magnet, and consequently the cone, to vibrate in and out, alternately increasing and reducing the pressure of the air (Figure 2.4a). The resulting pressure wave is called **longitudinal** because the variations in pressure are along the axis of the wave, that is the imaginary line between the sound source and the ear. However, we can represent the wave in the more familiar way shown in Figure 2.2 (Box 2.1) if we plot the pressure change against distance (Figure 2.4b).

Box 2.1   Waves

Both hearing and, as we shall see shortly, vision involve signals that are waves. A wave is a constantly repeating variation in some property, for example pressure as in a sound wave, and can be represented graphically (Figure 2.2). The horizontal axis is distance, and the length between one maximum and the next is called the **wavelength**. Figure 2.2 represents the variations in pressure in *space* at a particular time as the sound wave travels from its source. The maximum increase (or decrease) from the equilibrium value is called the **amplitude**. We can also represent the wave as variations in time at a particular point in space (Figure 2.3). Now it is a time interval between

one maximum and the next, not a distance, and this is called the **period** of the wave. The reciprocal of the period, that is 1/period, is called the **frequency**. For example, if the period of the wave is 0.01 second, the frequency is 1/0.01 or 100 hertz (Hz). (The unit of frequency is hertz, equivalent to cycles per second, a cycle being the repeat unit of the wave.) The wavelength and the frequency of a wave are connected by the speed at which the wave travels through the medium, usually air for sound. The equation that relates these three properties is

speed (in metres per second) = wavelength (in metres) × frequency (in hertz)

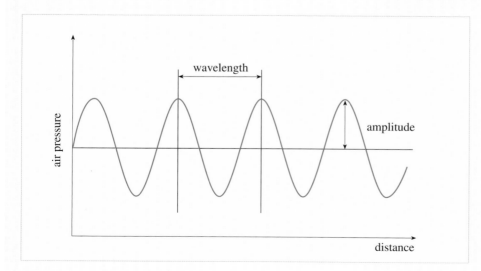

Figure 2.2   A sound wave represented as the variation in pressure with distance at a particular time.

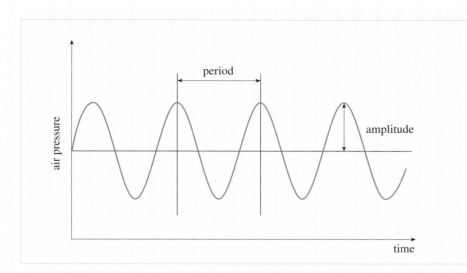

Figure 2.3   A sound wave represented as the variation in pressure with time at a particular point in space.

The two figures look very similar, and the subtle difference between them can be confusing. It may help to imagine that you are standing in the sea just offshore and watching the waves crashing one after another onto the beach. Figure 2.2 corresponds to the whole series of waves stretching out away from the beach at any given instant, whereas Figure 2.3 corresponds to the way the height of the water varies with time at the point where you are standing.

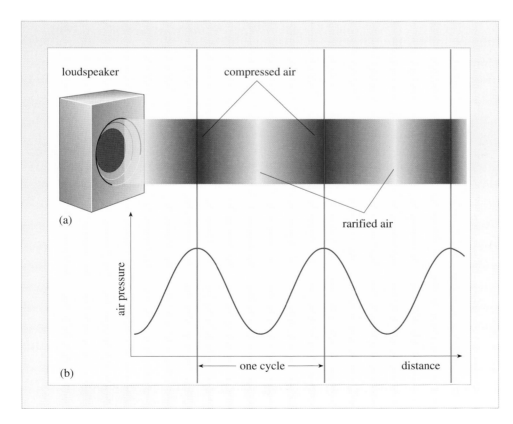

Figure 2.4   The production of sound waves by variations in air pressure (a) the variations in pressure produced by a loudspeaker cone; (b) the graphical representation of the pressure variation with distance.

The relationship between the wavelength of a sound wave and its frequency is determined by the speed of sound (Box 2.1). As the speed of sound in air varies slightly, depending on the temperature, atmospheric pressure and humidity, the usual standard to take is the value in dry air at 20 °C (293 K) and atmospheric pressure. This has a value of 343 metres per second (m s^{-1}). The equation that relates the wavelength λ, the frequency f, and the speed of sound c is (Box 2.1)

$$c = \lambda \times f \quad (1)$$

This can also be written in a form that shows how to calculate the wavelength from the frequency

$$\lambda = c / f \quad (2)$$

or an equivalent form to calculate the frequency from the wavelength.

$$f = c / \lambda \quad (3)$$

So, using formula (2), the wavelength of a note with a frequency of 262 Hz (middle C on a piano or electronic keyboard) is calculated to be 1.31 m (343 / 262 = 1.31).

○   What is the wavelength of a note with frequency 1000 Hz?

●   It is 0.343 m. This is calculated by dividing 343 m s^{-1} by 1000 Hz to give the answer in metres.

For the purposes of understanding hearing, the representation shown in Figure 2.3 is most useful. In terms of the loudspeaker illustration, that is a representation of the variation in time of the pressure at a single point, say at the front of the loudspeaker case. The resulting graph is called a **sound waveform**. The purest sound corresponds to the mathematical function called a sine wave, which can be produced by an electronic synthesiser. The waveform shown in Figure 2.3 is a sine wave. The sound made by a tuning fork, used as a standard of frequency by piano tuners, approximates a sine wave (though increasingly tuning forks are being replaced by electronic tuning aids).

The frequency determines the **pitch** of the sound (or **note** in musical language): the higher the frequency, the higher the pitch of the note. The note called middle C on a piano or keyboard has a frequency of 262 Hz, with the highest note a female singer is capable of reaching having a frequency of about 1000 Hz (or 1 kHz) and the lowest note that a male singer can reach being around 55 Hz.

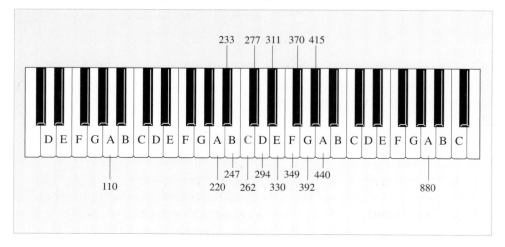

Figure 2.5   The notes on a keyboard with their frequencies. The note known as middle C is shown in red.

When two notes are sounded at the same time, whether the resultant effect is pleasing or discordant depends on the relationship between the frequencies of the sounds. For example if a sound of a particular frequency is played together with one of double the frequency, the effect is pleasant, with the combined sound being more interesting in effect. In musical terminology, the two notes are then said to be an **octave** apart. If sound waves with other frequencies related to the first by a simple ratio, for example 2 : 3 or 3 : 4, are added in, the sound changes, but continues to be pleasant. However, if sounds with frequencies that have no simple arithmetic relationship are sounded together, the effect is usually discordant. The sounds with frequencies related to a given note as simple multiples (×2, ×3, ×4, etc.) are called **overtones** of the original note. The original note is called the **fundamental**. The set of fundamental and overtones are called **harmonics**: the fundamental is the first harmonic, the first overtone is the second harmonic, and so on. The effect of adding the waveforms of the first two overtones to that of the fundamental is shown in Figure 2.6.

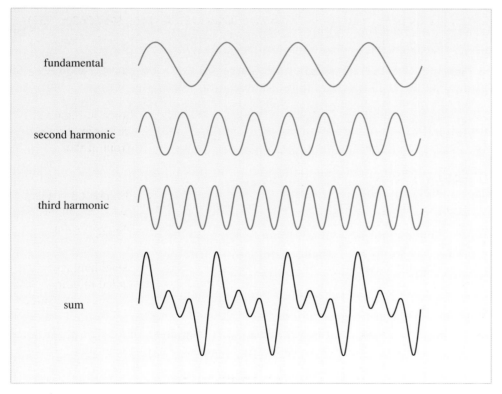

Figure 2.6   Adding together equal proportions of a fundamental plus the first two overtones.

The waveforms produced by a selection of musical instruments are shown in Figure 2.7 (overleaf). These are much more complex and no longer seem to bear any relationship to sine waves. You will learn later in the course that in fact any such complex waveform can be analysed into a series of sine waves added together (albeit in some cases a very long series involving a lot of harmonics). This process is called Fourier analysis, and with appropriate computer programs can be carried out very quickly and easily. It is the particular mix of all these different tones together with the fundamental that gives each instrument its characteristic musical quality, and is responsible for the particularly beautiful sound of a Stradivarius violin, for example. When Fourier analysis is applied to the waveforms from these various instruments, it is apparent that none of them produce sounds that consist only of the

Figure 2.7   The waveforms produced by various musical instruments.

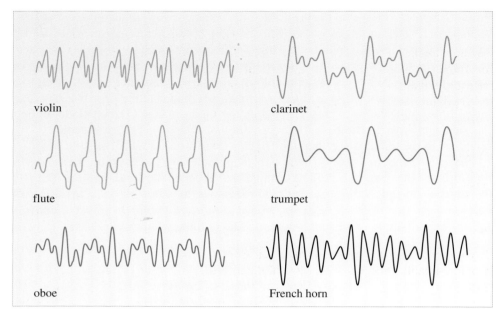

fundamental note; they all contain various harmonics. It is the physical properties (size, mass, materials) of the various instruments that determine the precise mix of harmonics produced; this is also why their frequencies are related by simple multiples to that of the fundamental.

You will learn much more about hearing in Block 3.

STUDY FILE

Activity 2.1   Sound wave superposition

You should now undertake this DVD activity which will allow you to listen to the sound of various waveforms, to add waveforms together, and to listen to the result. Before doing so, read Question 2.1, which you should be able to answer once you have completed the activity. Further instructions are given in the Block 1 Study File.

Question 2.1

By listening to two notes one after the other, what is the smallest frequency difference that you can detect? Does this depend on the frequencies of the notes used?

Question 2.2

Which of the following statements relating to sound and hearing are true and which false?

(a) Pure tones are those that have the shape of a sine wave. T

(b) If the fundamental frequency of a complex tone is 300 Hz, the second harmonic will have a frequency of 900 Hz. If 2nd harmonic = 1st overtone

(c) At a constant temperature and pressure, high frequency tones travel through air faster than low frequency ones. $v = f\lambda$

(d) Playing two notes with frequencies of 262 Hz and 294 Hz together would be expected to be less pleasant than two notes with frequencies of 262 Hz and 330 Hz played together.

Question 2.3

Sound reproduction systems produce stereophonic sound by using (at least) two separate loudspeakers. Is the ability to locate particular sounds, for example an instrument in an orchestra, that stereophonic sound affords likely to be purely an effect of the differences between the signals reaching the two ears, purely a result of perception, or both?   *Both*

Question 2.4

Attempt to frame two or three questions that the above introduction raises in your mind about the sense of hearing. Then compare yours with the questions given in the answer section at the end of the block.

What is role of perception - role of physics?

Why do we perceive some sounds as pleasant + others as unpleasant?

2.2 Vision

If you were to ask the question which sense is the most important, most people would probably choose vision. Most of the information we acquire about our surroundings results from sight, and most of our memories are based on visual experiences. For those people who are fortunate to enjoy good sight, the process of 'seeing' seems to involve almost no effort, it simply involves opening your eyes. Yet it is a process that is so complex and requiring such massive computational power that attempts to mimic the way the human brain can recognize shape, colour, three-dimensionality and motion are still quite primitive by comparison.

Many people would probably liken vision to the operation of a camera, and there are certainly a number of similarities in the initial stages whereby the signal strikes the receptors. But there the similarity ends, and the information processing that then takes place is amazingly complicated. Almost every aspect of vision gives rise to a whole series of questions about just how it works. Fortunately, despite its complexity, of all the senses, vision is perhaps the one that is best understood and about which most is known. It is partly for this reason that we have devoted the largest proportion of the course to vision, and in Block 4 you will spend four weeks studying the various aspects of this particular sense. For now, we shall concentrate mainly on the signal, and just begin to consider a few of the questions based on everyday experience that naturally arise once you move beyond the most superficial consideration of the visual system.

Earlier, we stated that the process of sensation consists of two overlapping stages, reception of the signal and perception, and that the signal required for sight is light. The light may be reflected from or, in some cases such as traffic lights or a television, emitted by the object being looked at.

○   Where are the receptors for sight located?

●   Nearly everyone knows that these are in the eye, though perhaps few would know exactly where in the eye the interaction takes place.

The process of seeing begins with light entering the eye via the cornea and the lens (Figure 2.8, overleaf). These focus an image of the object on the retina at the back of the eye where the receptors are located. Just as with a camera, the image formed on the retina is upside-down; as part of the information processing involved in vision, the brain perceives this as being the 'right way up'. The conversion of the light signal into electrical signals that are transmitted to the brain then takes place in the retina.

Figure 2.8   A simplified diagram of the human eye.

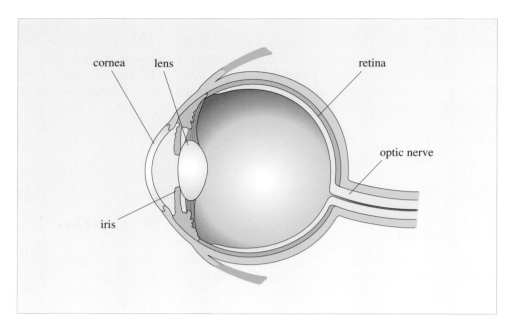

The aspect of vision that we shall focus on here is the ability to see in colour. In order to understand how this works, you need first to understand the nature of light, and also to explore some of the physical aspects of colour.

○   First then, what is light?

●   Light is a form of energy that can be described in two ways, either as 'packets' called photons, or as a wave. For now we will concentrate on the wave description.

Visible light is an electromagnetic wave with a wavelength in the range 380–780 nm (1 nm = 10^{-9} m; Figure 2.9). Other electromagnetic waves that will be familiar to you are radio waves, microwaves and infrared that have longer wavelengths, and ultraviolet light, X-rays and gamma rays that have shorter wavelengths, than visible

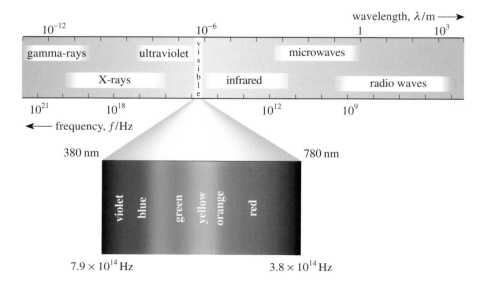

Figure 2.9   Visible light and the electromagnetic spectrum.

light. They are called electromagnetic because the wave consists of simultaneous periodic variations in the electric and magnetic fields at right angles to each other at a particular point (Figure 2.10). In contrast to sound waves, the electric and magnetic fields involved do not require any transmitting medium, and so light can travel through space. Because the two are always in step with one another, we only need to consider one of the oscillations when focusing on the wavelength of light. Note that because the oscillations are at right angles to the direction of travel, light is a **transverse** wave, as opposed to sound, which is a longitudinal wave.

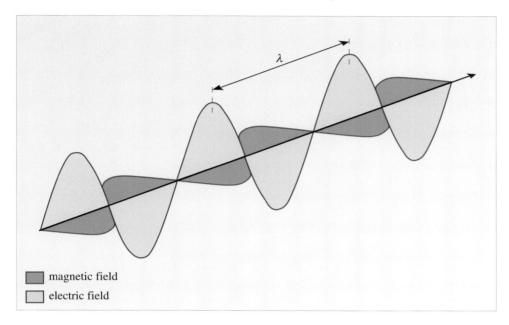

magnetic field
electric field

Figure 2.10 An electromagnetic wave.

The relationship between the wavelength of a light wave and its frequency is determined by the speed of light. The speed of light in a vacuum is exactly 299 792 458 m s^{-1} (this is how the metre is now defined). Light is slowed to a greater or lesser extent when it passes through transparent substances such as air, water or glass. (When we consider vision in Block 4 the implications of this will be discussed in more detail.) For our current purposes, the extent to which light is slowed by passing through air can be ignored, and we can take the speed of light in air to be approximately 3×10^8 m s^{-1}.

The equation that relates the frequency f, the wavelength λ and the speed of light c is the same as that for sound (with the speed of sound replaced by the speed of light).

$f = c / \lambda$

So, using this formula, the frequency of light of wavelength 700 nm is 4.3×10^{14} Hz.

○ What is the frequency of light with wavelength 400 nm?

● It is 7.5×10^{14} Hz. This is calculated by dividing 3×10^8 m s^{-1} by 400×10^{-9} m (note that we need to use the same units of length, in this case metres, for the speed and wavelength) to give the answer in units of s^{-1}, that is Hz.

The eye is sensitive just to the very narrow range of wavelengths between 380–780 nm. Exposure to shorter wavelengths, although they cannot be seen, does cause damage to the eye that is usually irreversible. Exposure to longer wavelengths may or may not be harmful, depending on the wavelength.

Figure 2.11 The visible
spectrum.

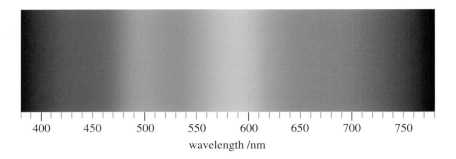

wavelength /nm

The wavelength of light determines its colour (Figure 2.11).

○ Using Figure 2.11, what is the approximate wavelength of yellow light?

● Yellow light has a wavelength of around 580 nm (580×10^{-9} m or 5.8×10^{-7} m).

As mentioned above, the process of seeing begins with light entering the eye.
Objects that do not themselves emit light rely on light being reflected from the sun
or some other light source such as a light bulb or fluorescent tube. When some such
illuminating source is no longer present, such objects cannot be seen. However,
objects that give out light themselves, such as a neon advertising display, and TV or
computer screens, do not rely on reflected light. In considering the colour of an
object, there is an important distinction between whether it reflects light or emits
light itself.

Suppose you are looking at a computer screen that has been arranged just to be
blank but entirely blue in colour. It is *emitting* blue light, and that is what enters the
eye. But when you look at a sheet of blue coloured paper (assume it is the same
shade of blue), it *reflects* blue light into the eye. The difference is that sunlight (or
white light from a light bulb) illuminates the paper, and the dye or pigment on the
paper *absorbs* the other wavelengths, leaving only the blue to be reflected. This
distinction is of crucial importance when considering how different colours are
produced, on the one hand, on a TV or computer screen and, on the other, in inks,
dyes and paints.

We shall begin by considering emitted light, for example as from a TV screen
(Figure 2.12). It has been known for many years that you can create any colour by
mixing various proportions of the three **primary colours** red, green and blue. These
are called the **additive primary colours**. If you mix equal proportions (intensities)
of red and blue, the result is magenta; mixing equal proportions of blue and green
gives cyan (a kind of turquoise); and, perhaps the most surprising result, equal
proportions of green and red give yellow (Figure 2.13). You can get an impression of
this process from the red-green grid shown in Figure 2.14: the right-hand grid (b)
with the smaller size cell looks perceptibly yellow, while the red and green cells are
much more apparent in the left-hand grid (a).

Note that mixing equal proportions of red, green and blue lights gives white light.
Since green and blue mixed together gives cyan, that is equivalent to saying that
mixing red light and cyan light gives white light. These are said to be
complementary colours. To put it another way, cyan is the complementary colour
of red because that is the colour remaining when red is removed from white light.
Similarly, green and magenta are complementary colours, as are blue and yellow.

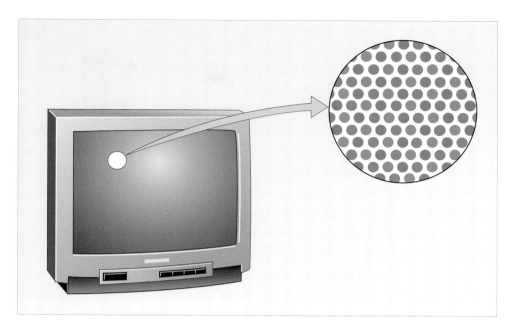

Figure 2.12   A colour television set showing the layout of the 'pixels'. 'Pixel' is short for 'picture element'. On a television set or computer monitor, each pixel is composed of three dots: a red, a blue and a green.

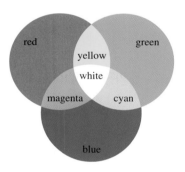

Figure 2.13   The additive primary colours red, green and blue, combining in pairs to give cyan, magenta and yellow, and all three to give white.

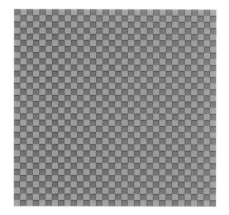

Figure 2.14   A red-green grid with two different cell sizes; the squares in (b) have one-sixteenth the area of those in (a). Note that this only works because, even in (b) the squares are still red and green, and they each reflect red and green light respectively. If instead we had mixed the inks used to produce the red and green squares the result would not have been yellow.

Activity 2.2   Colour mixing

You should now undertake this DVD activity which will allow you to explore the proportions of the red, green and blue additive primaries for a range of pre-set colours. You can then go on to mix your own colours to gain experience of the effect of adding various proportions of the three primaries. Before doing so, read Questions 2.5 and 2.6, which you should be able to answer once you have completed the activity. Further instructions are given in the Block 1 Study File.

Question 2.5

This question relates to the additive primary colours red, green and blue.

(a) What is the smallest amount of green added to red that gives a perceptibly different colour?

(b) What is the smallest decrease in the green component of yellow that gives a perceptibly different colour?

Comment on your observations.

Question 2.6

Most computers allow 256 different levels of each of the three additive primary colours, giving a total of $256 \times 256 \times 256$, that is 16 777 216, possible colours. If you were offered a cheaper computer that only gave 128 different levels of each primary colour, would you notice the difference in the range of colours it could display?

If you have ever tried to mix paints to get a particular colour, you probably know that mixing red paint and green paint produces a muddy brown colour, not yellow. You also may know that colour inkjet printers, now a common accessory if you have a computer, use cyan, magenta and yellow inks. These are called the **subtractive primary colours**.

○   Do you notice any connection between the additive primary colours and the subtractive primary colours?

●   The subtractive primary colours are the same colours obtained by mixing two of the additive primaries.

If you combine the subtractive primaries in pairs, you get the three additive primary colours (Figure 2.15). This is not too surprising if you think about it carefully. Take cyan and yellow as an example. An object that is coloured cyan absorbs red light (its complementary colour) and reflects blue and green light. An object that is coloured yellow absorbs blue light and reflects red and green light. If you mix cyan paint with yellow paint and use that to paint something, the paint will now absorb both red light and blue light, leaving only green light to reflect. Hence, mixing the two subtractive primaries cyan and yellow gives green (Figure 2.15).

You will learn much more about colour and colour vision in Block 4.

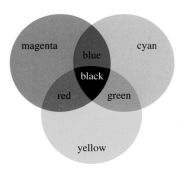

Figure 2.15   The subtractive primary colours cyan, magenta and yellow, combining in pairs to give red, green and blue, and all three combining to give black.

Question 2.7

Which of the following statements relating to colour vision are true and which false?

(a) Green light is of shorter wavelength than yellow light. *T*

(b) Magenta is the complementary colour of blue.

(c) On a computer with 256 levels of each primary colour, a mixture with red = 100, green = 100 and blue = 100 produces a darker grey than a mixture with red = 200, green = 200 and blue = 200. (Grey is produced by a mixture of equal amounts of the three primary colours with an intensity lower then the maximum of 255.)

(d) A colour printer uses a mixture of magenta and green inks to produce the colour blue. *+   magenta + cyan*

Question 2.8

Attempt to frame two or three questions that the above description raises in your mind about the phenomenon of colour vision. Then compare yours with the questions given in the answer section at the end of the block.

What part of the eye detects colour?

Are there individual receptors for different colours of light? Are they the subtractive primary colours? Does the brain interpret proportions to determine overall colour?

2.3 Touch and pain

Touch and pain are the most familiar of the senses that make up the **somatic sensory** (or **somatosensory**) **system**, sometimes known as the **bodily senses**. Though sharing certain features in common, they do differ substantially in operation, so let us begin by considering touch. Whereas the receptors for vision and hearing are located in quite specific places, the receptors for touch are widely dispersed. Touch receptors are located on virtually every external part of our bodies. There is another difference relating to the signals: vision and hearing are long-distance senses; touch is a proximal sense, you have to be in contact with the object you are touching.

○   What is the signal for the sense of touch?

●   In order to touch something you have to press on it or it on you, thereby slightly deforming the skin. The signal is therefore pressure.

Though superficially quite different, the receptors involved in the sense of touch have much in common with those of hearing. You may recall that sound consists of waves that involve a regular variation in pressure. In fact, both sound and touch involve **mechanoreceptors** that transform variations in pressure into electrical signals.

Touch receptors are found all over the surface of our bodies, but their density does vary greatly.

○   Name one part of the body where you think the density of touch receptors is likely to be high, and one where you think it is likely to be low. *fingers*

●   The fingertips, lips and tongue all have high densities of receptors; the lower back, forearm and back of the hand have quite low densities.

The fingertips and tongue have around 100 receptors per cm^2, whereas the back of the hand has only about 10 receptors per cm^2.

Activity 2.3   Two-point threshold determination

You can measure the density of touch receptors for yourself using the two-point threshold test. You should now undertake this activity, which will require the assistance of a helper. It involves the determination of the minimum separation of two points of stimulation for various parts of the body that just produces two distinct impressions of touch, and below which only one sensation is felt. Instructions are given in the Block I Study File.

In Western society, the act of touching someone else is imbued with meaning and subject to a number of taboos. It either indicates affection and intimacy, from a friend or lover, or can be aggressive, such as being pushed or punched by an assailant. Though we tend to consider vision or hearing as being more important, touch sensations are the principal components of sexual activity. In some ways, touch is the most primitive of the senses: it literally defines the boundary between self and the outside world. Yet it is remarkably sensitive and sophisticated. You can easily detect a faint breeze, or a small insect landing on your skin (the receptors are often found close to a hair follicle so even if the skin is not touched directly, movement of the hair is detected).

Touch plays an important role in providing feedback as we move about, and it enables us to feel the texture of a surface and to recognize objects simply by feeling their shape. The sense of touch can even substitute in a limited way for the absence of sight. The development of a tactile alphabet by the 15-year-old Louis Braille, who was blinded at the age of four following an accident in his father's workshop, depends on the last quality. It uses an array of six dots, coded so that each symbol is represented by one or more of the dots being raised above the surface of the paper. There are different combinations of dots to represent the letters of the alphabet, numerals and even abbreviations for commonly used words (Figure 2.16). The use of Braille to allow blind people to read is now common throughout the world.

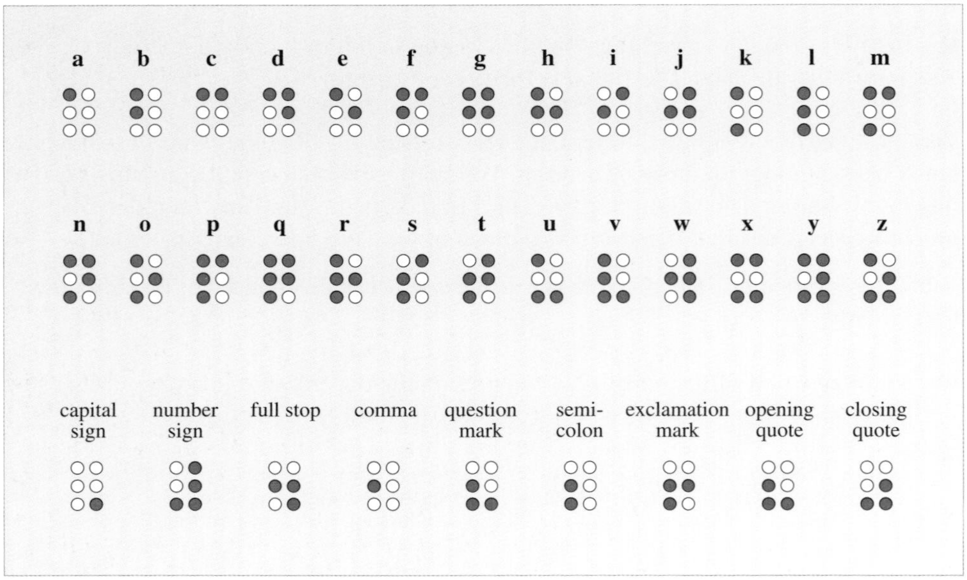

Figure 2.16   The Braille alphabet.

Though not as immediately obvious, there are also mechanoreceptors that provide us with the sense of where our limbs are in space at any moment and a sense of their movement. This is called **proprioception**; the sense of movement is called **kinesthesis** (or sometimes dynamic proprioception). You will learn more about proprioception in Block 5.

The sense of pain is qualitatively different from all the other senses. For all other senses, provided the stimulus is not excessively strong, the resulting perception can often be pleasing: looking at a great painting or beautiful countryside, listening to a favourite piece of music, stroking a pet cat or dog, smelling a rose or participating in a wine tasting all bring various degrees of enjoyment. However, (except for masochists) experiencing pain is always unpleasant. This is not surprising since it is the body's alarm system. The occurrence of pain signifies injury to the relevant part of the body. The receptors that respond to such stimuli are called **nociceptors**.

Nociceptors are distributed throughout the body, not just on its surface. The signal that stimulates them involves some type of tissue damage. However, the perception of pain is a highly individual and subjective sensation, and it is this that makes it particularly difficult to understand, and hence to define and to treat. Injury does not always give rise to pain, at least not immediately. There is the story of an army officer who was skiing with his unit when the ground gave way and he fell into a narrow crevasse. He became wedged so that he could not move his legs and one of his arms was also stuck fast above his head. However, he felt no pain until an hour after the accident. It was only later that he was discovered to have dislocated his shoulder, broken his collar bone and sustained severe bruises of his legs and lower abdomen. This type of experience is not uncommon, particularly if the injured person's attention is distracted by other matters.

In contrast is the common experience of people who have lost a limb through amputation. Although the nociceptors can clearly no longer be present, a common experience of amputees is to still feel pain from the absent arm or leg, called **phantom limb pain**. To the sufferer, the pain that is felt is quite clearly localized in the missing limb.

Pain treatment is one of the major concerns of pharmaceutical companies world-wide. In 2000, the analgesics market alone was estimated to be worth around $8.8 billion and growing at a rate of approximately 8% per annum. It has also been estimated that 100 billion (10^{11}) aspirin tablets alone are taken every year. In addition to the use of drugs, there is increasing use of alternative strategies such as hypnosis, yoga or acupuncture (Figure 2.17), though little is yet known about the mechanism by which these methods relieve pain.

The role of acute pain in indicating the site of injury or malfunction can readily be seen. However, the occurrence of persistent, chronic pain would seem to be less useful as an alarm, and its management, say for those terminally ill with cancer, is one of the most difficult aspects of treating such patients. One of the commonly used drugs to relieve cancer pain is morphine. It was during research to investigate how morphine and other opium-related drugs relieve pain that the scientists discovered endogenous opiates, that is pain-relieving substances produced by the body itself, which were termed **endorphins**. The endorphins are all members of the group of compounds called peptides, made of an assortment of amino acids strung together (Box 2.2, overleaf). In addition to exhibiting analgesic properties, the endorphins were shown to bind to the same molecular receptors as the externally administered opiates. These opiate receptors are particular regions of specialized protein

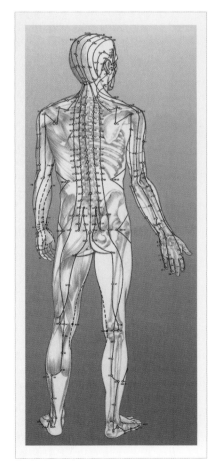

Figure 2.17   An acupuncture reference guide showing the posterior view of acupuncture point locations.

Box 2.2   Peptides and proteins

Proteins are one of the main classes of molecules of which living organisms are composed. Proteins have a diverse range of functions. By far the largest group of proteins are the enzymes, which are biological catalysts and bring about a wide variety of metabolic processes. Of particular relevance to the senses is the group of proteins whose function is to carry signals between cells or to form the receptors with which sensory signals interact.

Proteins are polymers, that is, large molecules made of hundreds or thousands of monomer units. The monomer units that make up proteins are called **amino acids**, of which there are twenty commonly occurring in proteins (Table 2.1). These can link together in virtually any sequence, which accounts for the almost limitless variety of proteins found in nature. **Peptides** are small fragments of proteins containing from two up to (say) fifty amino acid units.

The general structure of the natural amino acids is shown in Figure 2.18. They each have a central carbon atom to which is attached an amino group ($-NH_2$), a carboxylic acid group ($-CO_2H$), a hydrogen atom, and a fourth group designated as R which differs for each amino acid. (There is just one exception to this, which is proline, where the R group forms a ring with the other end attached to the nitrogen of the amino group, meaning this only has one hydrogen atom attached.)

In proteins and peptides the amino acid monomer units are linked together by a bond between the carbon atom of the carboxylic acid group of one amino acid and the nitrogen atom of the amino group of another. When the bond is formed, the $-OH$ of the carboxylic acid group and one hydrogen atom from the amino group are removed (Figure 2.19).

The symbols given in Table 2.1 are used to denote the amino acid unit (known as a residue) in peptides or proteins, that is the amino acid structure minus the carboxylic acid $-OH$ and amino $-H$. As an example, the two possible dipeptides containing alanine and valine would be denoted as H–Ala-Val–OH and H–Val-Ala–OH.

You will come across peptides and proteins on a number of other occasions through the course.

Table 2.1   The names and symbols of the twenty amino acids commonly found in proteins.

Name	Symbol	Name	Symbol
alanine	Ala	leucine	Leu
arginine	Arg	lysine	Lys
asparagine	Asn	methionine	Met
aspartic acid	Asp	phenylalanine	Phe
cysteine	Cys	proline	Pro
glutamic acid	Glu	serine	Ser
glutamine	Gln	threonine	Thr
glycine	Gly	tryptophan	Trp
histidine	His	tyrosine	Tyr
isoleucine	Ile	valine	Val

Figure 2.18   The general structure of the amino acids found in proteins. C is carbon, H is hydrogen, N is nitrogen, O is oxygen and R is one of 20 different possible groups.

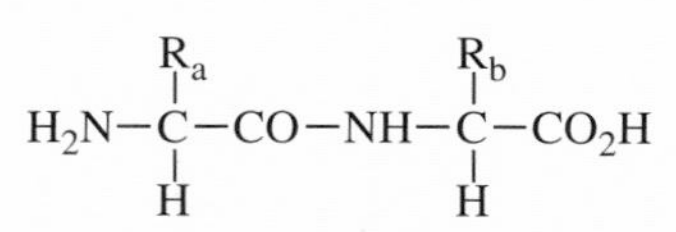

Figure 2.19   The general structure of a dipeptide.

molecules (Box 2.2). The molecular structures of two of the substances found, called **enkephalins**, are shown in Figure 2.20. The two enkephalins are made up of just five amino acid residues (they are therefore called pentapeptides), of which the first four are identical. Studies using other synthetic pentapeptides have shown that all four amino acids are necessary to retain the analgesic properties of these test substances.

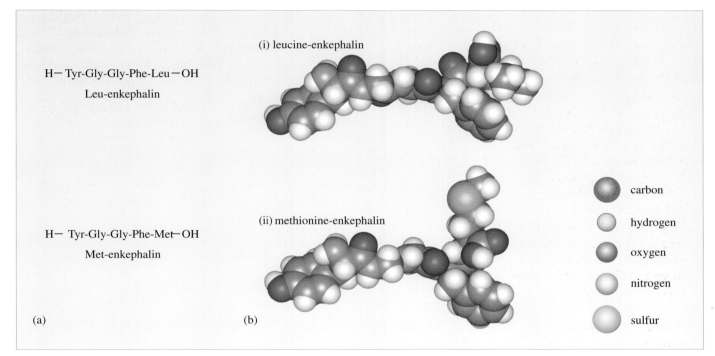

Figure 2.20   (a) Structures using the symbols for amino acid residues of the two enkephalins found to act as the body's own analgesics; (b) molecular models of the two enkephalins.

Question 2.9

Which of the following statements relating to the somatic sensory system are true and which false?

(a) The fingertips are more sensitive than the back of the hand because the mechanoreceptors are located nearer to the surface of the skin in the former case.

(b) In the Braille alphabet, the symbols for a question mark and an opening quote mark are only differentiated by their position on the grid of the standard cell.

(c) The discovery of the role of endorphins within the body means that the placebo effect – the perceived relief of pain by the use of tablets that do not contain any medicinal drug – might not be wholly psychological.

(d) The only difference in the structure of peptides and proteins is that the former are smaller.

Question 2.10

Attempt to frame two or three questions that the above description raises in your mind about the somatic sensory system. Then compare yours with the questions given in the answer section at the end of the block.

2.4 Smell and taste

Of all the senses, smell and taste are in many ways the least well understood. In contrast to vision and hearing, and even touch and pain, it is a lot more difficult to quantify smell and taste: they are much more subjective. Consequently, while it is possible for two people to agree on the colour of a particular object (assuming that neither is colour deficient), in comparing smells the language used is much less precise. The best that can be done is to make comparison with familiar recognizable smells – earthy, fruity, floral, medicinal – always remembering that these in themselves may arise from a mixture of chemical compounds. Literally thousands of substances have characteristic fragrances. At Versailles in France, there is even a museum of smells – the Osmothèque.

Finding a method of classifying smells has long provided a challenge. One such classification used by perfumers when describing the different ingredients used to manufacture perfumes divides fragrances into top, middle and end 'notes' (Table 2.2). The 'top notes' are the most volatile components that are the most immediately noticeable, and these usually have citrus and herb-like scents. The main effect of the perfume derives from the floral scented 'middle notes', with the less volatile woody, musky 'end notes' providing the lingering effect, which evaporates only slowly.

Similarly, in wine tasting, for example, a very florid, but individual, vocabulary is used such as the following description of a Californian Chardonnay (a white wine):

> Its tiers of ripe pear, fig, honey flavours are framed by smoky, toasty oak. An altogether complex and beautifully crafted wine with a rich butterscotch aftertaste.
>
> Tasting notes on the *Wine Spectator* magazine website.

or to describe an Australian Shiraz (a red wine):

> Flavours of plum, blackberry, chocolate and pepper, with hints of cedar, liquorice and mint swirling through the exotic finish that unfold and gain complexity and nuance on the finish.
>
> Tasting notes on the *Wine Spectator* magazine website.

If we consider the signal that gives rise to smell and taste it is apparent why there is this difference between, on the one hand, these two senses and, on the other, say, the senses of vision and hearing. The signals involved in vision and hearing are both waves, and these have both wavelengths and amplitudes that can be measured. These are the parameters that determine the nature of the experience for both senses. In contrast, for both smell and taste the signal is a number of molecules of the substance(s) concerned, and for each substance its constituent molecules are identical but different from the molecules of every other substance. Further, it is not obvious what property of the molecule determines the smell or taste. It is because molecules are involved that smell and taste are often known as the **chemical senses**.

Smell and taste are also more prone to **adaptation**. Adaptation of a sensory experience is the fading of the sensation with time so that eventually one is no longer aware of it. For example, on entering an unfamiliar room, it is often possible

Table 2.2   Some common substances used as ingredients in perfumery.

Note	Source	Substance	Physical property*
top			
	galbanum (leafy)	undecanal (green)	liquid, b.t. 117 °C
	lemongrass	citral, a mixture of	
		geranial	liquid, b.t. 118 °C
		neral	liquid, b.t. 120 °C
	citrus oils	limonene	liquid, b.t. 178 °C
	peppermint	menthol (cool/minty)	solid, m.t. 43 °C
	coriander	linalool	liquid, b.t. 198 °C
	lavender	linalyl acetate	liquid, b.t. 220 °C
	spearmint	carvone	liquid, b.t. 230 °C
middle			
	rose	nerol (rosy, orange blossom)	liquid, b.t. 224 °C
		geraniol (floral)	liquid, b.t. 230 °C
	lily	citronellol (rosy)	liquid, b.t. 244 °C
	violet	butylcyclohexyl acetate (floral, woody)	liquid, b.t. 232 °C
	jasmine	*cis*-jasmone, methyl dihydrojasmonate	liquid, b.t. 118 °C
end			
	vanilla	vanillin	solid, m.t. 82 °C
	musk	butyl nitrobenzenes (musk xylene)	solid, m.t. 114 °C
	vetiver	vetivone	solid, m.t. 51 °C

*b.t. boiling temperature; m.t. melting temperature. Liquids with low boiling temperatures are more volatile than those with higher boiling temperatures. Generally, solids are even less volatile, although there are exceptions such as menthol. The volatility is only one factor involved, hence the classification of lavender and spearmint as top notes and jasmine as a middle note. You will learn more about perfumes in Block 6.

to detect a characteristic odour, but after being there for a short time, it apparently disappears. That it is still present is easily shown by leaving the room for a while and then returning when the odour is once more detectable. It is also the case that our perception of the same food or drink varies depending on a range of other factors such as location (presence of other odours), time of day (before or after a meal), and history (whether you have just partaken of any strongly flavoured food or drink). This is encapsulated in the advice when buying or selling wine to buy after eating an apple, when only the best wines will still taste good, and to offer some cheese when selling wine, as this tends to make even ordinary wine appear better quality.

○   Where do you think the smell receptors are?

●   They are situated in the uppermost reaches of the nasal cavity.

In fact they are directly attached to the brain (Figure 2.21); indeed the olfactory bulb is arguably the only part of the brain that is directly accessible to the environment.

Figure 2.21   The anatomy of the olfactory system.

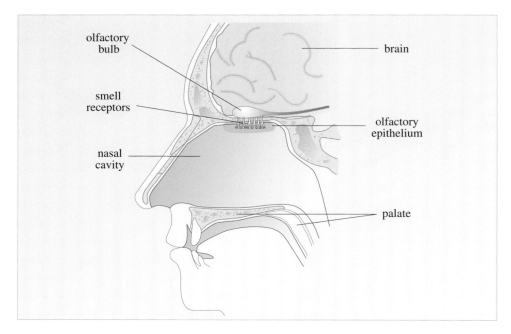

The sense of smell involves sniffing, which causes air containing molecules of the odorous substance(s) to pass over the olfactory receptor cells. Molecules of odorous materials dissolve in the moisture of the lining of the nose, and interact with the olfactory receptors. These receptors are cavities formed by particular parts of protein molecules into which certain molecules fit, and it is this process that triggers an electrical signal. Accordingly, because of this mechanism, one of the major determinants of the odour of a molecule seems to be its shape. It is also apparent that only volatile substances have odours, since it is necessary for the molecules to be carried through the air.

The complexity of our sense of smell is illustrated by the following quotation from the *Wine Spectator* magazine: *

> The world of smell is vast and bewildering. First of all, our olfactory equipment is incredibly sensitive; we can distinguish aromas in quantities so small that laboratory equipment can scarcely measure them. Second, our analytic capacity is extraordinary; estimates of the number of different smells humans can identify range up to 10,000! Finally, wine has a staggering number of smellable elements. In their exhaustive study *Wines: Their Sensory Evaluation*, Maynard Amerine and Edward Roessler, both professors at the University of California, write that 'Identified in wine aromas are at least 181 esters, 52 alcohols,

*Do not worry if you are not familiar with the some of the terms such as esters, aldehydes, and ketones; these are just different families of chemical compounds the molecules of which share particular structural features.

75 aldehydes and ketones, 22 acetals, 18 lactones, six secondary acetamides, 29 nitrogen-containing compounds, 18 sulfur-containing compounds, two ethers, 11 furans and 18 epoxides, as well as 30 miscellaneous compounds. Many of these are modified in various ways by ageing and cellar treatment, and they can and do react with each other or have additive, masking or synergistic properties.'

'The ABCs of Wine Tasting' by Thomas Matthews, *Wine Spectator*, 30 September, 1996.

This quotation, relating as it does to wine *tasting*, yet dealing with the sense of *smell* illustrates another important fact, namely that the senses of smell and taste are intimately linked. Our sense of taste is relatively basic and is greatly enhanced by our sense of smell. Most people will have noticed how uninteresting food tastes when you have a cold that temporarily takes away the sense of smell. In fact there is general agreement that there are just five basic tastes: sweet, sour, salt, bitter and umami (the 'meaty' flavour of monosodium glutamate or MSG).

○   Where do you think the taste receptors are?

●   The taste receptors are largely situated on the tongue, with some further down the throat (Figure 2.22).

Just as one can smell only those molecules that dissolve in the moisture in the lining of the nose, one can only taste substances that dissolve in the secretions in the mouth. The interaction between the molecules being tasted and the taste receptors are thought to be very similar to those involved in the sense of smell.

It has only been with the advent of the techniques of molecular biology that scientists have been able to finally identify some at least of the receptors involved in smell and taste. The first smell receptors were identified by Linda Buck and her team at Harvard Medical School in 1991, and the first taste receptor was identified by Nirupa Chaudhari and her co-workers at the University of Miami School of

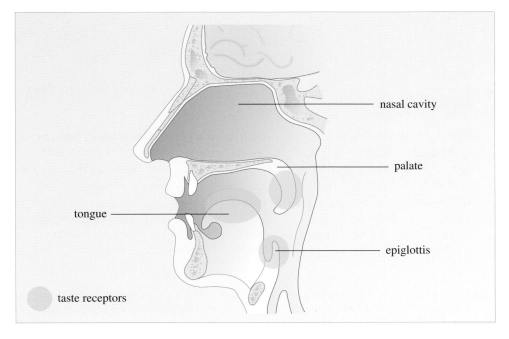

Figure 2.22   The anatomy of the gustatory system.

Medicine as recently as 2000. You will learn about the details of how these two senses work in Block 6. To conclude this section, we shall briefly examine one issue concerning the sense of smell.

It has been known for many years that insects, amphibians, reptiles and many mammals communicate with one another by emitting certain specific substances called **pheromones** that stimulate what is effectively a specialized sense of smell in the recipient. The most common type of message sent using pheromones concerns sexual receptivity. Naturally enough, there has been much speculation about the possibility that humans make use of pheromones, although the evidence until 2000 had been equivocal. Much of the research into human pheromones has been funded by perfume companies, since there would obviously be a huge market for perfumes containing the appropriate substances.

In 2000, neurobiologist Peter Mombaerts of the Rockefeller University in New York and his research team reported that they had located a gene very closely related to that for the pheromone receptor of a rodent, essentially a type of olfactory receptor. They initially found eight different human DNA sequences that resembled rodent sequences that encode for pheromone receptors, but seven turned out to be so-called 'pseudo-genes' that are unable to give rise to the production of an intact protein. However, the eighth definitely seemed to have the potential to produce a pheromone receptor. When the scientists studied tissue from the human nose, they indeed located the receptor corresponding to the gene they had identified. While the presence of such a receptor in the nose is a necessary condition for there to be one or more human pheromones, there is no guarantee that they actually exist. None the less, this discovery has provided fresh impetus to studies aimed at answering this question once and for all.

Question 2.11

Which of the following statements relating to smell and taste are true and which false?

(a) The smell of newly-sawn pine branches must be due to the sap in the tree rather than the wood itself.

(b) Attempts to make a deodorizer spray that contains molecules which combine with the malodorous molecules to change their size or shape would be unlikely to have the desired effect of eliminating a bad smell.

(c) The improvement in taste of food by the addition of small amounts of salt is an example of adaptation.

(d) The operation of a taste receptor is likely to be more similar to the action of an opiate receptor than to the action of a touch receptor.

Question 2.12

Attempt to frame two or three questions that the above description raises in your mind about the senses of smell and taste. Then compare yours with the questions given in the answer section at the end of the block.

2.5 The senses compared

From this brief survey of the human senses, you may well have noticed that they all share common features: in each case, there is a stimulus, which can take a number of forms, and there is a receptor, which is where the stimulus causes the creation of an electrical signal, the process called **transduction**. Table 2.3 summarizes the nature of the stimulus and the type of receptor involved for each of the senses or **sensory modalities**.

Table 2.3   The sensory modalities.

Modality	Form of stimulus	Type of receptor	Location of receptors
hearing	mechanical	mechanoreceptor	cochlea (inner ear)
balance	mechanical	mechanoreceptor	semicircular canals
vision	light	photoreceptor	retina (eye)
touch	mechanical	mechanoreceptor	skin
pressure	mechanical	mechanoreceptor	skin, deep tissue
temperature	thermal	thermoreceptor	skin
pain	mechanical, thermal, chemical	nociceptor	skin, internal organs
proprioception	mechanical	mechanoreceptor	muscles, tendons, joints
smell	chemical	chemoreceptor	upper nasal cavity (nose)
taste	chemical	chemoreceptor	tongue, pharynx, palate, epiglottis

Transduction involves an initial electrical event that gives rise to a receptor potential. This in turn brings about the transmission of action potentials (often called 'firing') along the connected neurons. You will learn in Block 2 that action potentials have very particular properties. They are essentially 'all-or-nothing' signals that do not diminish with distance along the neuron. They have a fixed size and duration, and so these properties cannot be used to encode information. Instead, it is a combination of the rate at which action potentials are generated, and the number and distribution of the neurons firing action potentials in a particular nerve that constitute the code used to transmit information to the brain. The fascinating details of this process will be revealed for each of the senses as you proceed through the course.

2.6 Summary of Section 2

The sense of hearing involves the sound signal impinging on the eardrum (tympanum) located in the middle ear, causing it to vibrate. The vibrations are transmitted to the cochlea in the inner ear, where the signal is transformed into electrical signals that are sent to the brain. Also located in the inner ear are the semicircular canals which are the organs of our sense of balance. Sound is produced by objects vibrating with a frequency in the range 20–20 000 Hz.

Sound is a longitudinal wave in which the variations in pressure are along the direction of propagation. A plot of the pressure change against time is called the waveform of the sound. The purest sound is when the waveform has the shape of a sine wave. Most musical instruments produce more complex waveforms, but these can be analysed as a series of harmonics (sine waves of different frequencies related by simple multiples).

The sense of vision begins with light entering the eye via the cornea and the lens, which focuses an image on the retina. The image formed on the retina is upside-down; as part of the information processing involved in vision, the brain perceives this as being the 'right way up'. The conversion of the light signal into electrical signals that are transmitted to the brain then takes place in the retina.

Light is an electromagnetic wave, which is a transverse wave, in contrast to sound waves. Only light waves with a wavelength in the range 380–780 nm are visible to humans. Objects that do not themselves emit light rely on light being reflected from the sun or some other light source. When the illuminating source is no longer present, such objects cannot be seen. However, objects that give out light themselves do not rely on reflected light.

The wavelength of light determines its colour. In considering the colour of an object, there is an important distinction between whether it reflects light or emits light itself. This distinction is of crucial importance when considering how different colours are produced.

It has been known for many years that you can create any colour by mixing various proportions of three primary colours. For emitted light, these are red, green and blue, the additive primary colours. For reflected light, these are cyan, magenta and yellow, the subtractive primary colours. Each additive primary has one of the subtractive primaries as its complementary colour.

Touch and pain are the most familiar of the senses that make up the somatic sensory system. The signal for touch is pressure. Touch receptors, which are mechanoreceptors, are found all over the surface of our bodies, with some areas having much higher densities than others. Touch plays an important role in providing feedback as we move about, particularly through receptors that indicate the position and movement of our limbs (proprioception and kinesthesis respectively).

The occurrence of pain signifies tissue damage, the receptors that respond to such stimuli being called nociceptors. Nociceptors are distributed throughout the body. Injury does not always give rise to immediate pain, and conversely, people who have lost a limb through amputation often experience so-called phantom limb pain. Pain treatment is a major human activity. The body also produces its own pain-relieving substances, called endorphins, which are peptides.

Smell and taste are often called the chemical senses because they require molecular interactions as a stimulus. The interaction of molecules of the substance(s) with receptors in the nasal cavity or on the tongue stimulates the sense of smell or taste respectively. Molecular shape seems to be a major determinant of odour, and probably of taste also. The senses of smell and taste are intimately linked, with our sense of taste being greatly enhanced by our sense of smell. Like many other animals, humans may have an auxiliary sense of smell that responds to pheromones.

All the senses or sensory modalities share common features: in each case, there is a stimulus, in the form of mechanical energy, thermal energy, light energy or chemical energy involving molecular interactions, and a receptor, which is where the stimulus causes the creation of a receptor potential, which affects the generation of action potentials in connected neurons. A combination of the rate with which action potentials are generated, and the number and distribution of the neurons firing in a particular nerve constitutes the code used to transmit information to the brain.

Question 2.13

Compare and contrast the initial stage of sensation for each of the senses of hearing and smell.

Smell - chemical, dissolved in moisture in nose, stimulates chemical receptor → send electrical signals to brain

hearing. sound wave mechanical input on ear drum → inner ear to cochlea sends electrical signals to brain

Similarity - environmental process stimulates Receptors to send electrical signals to brain

molecules
difference - smell involves chemicals + chemical receptors
hearing involves mechanical input + mechanical receptors

Illusions and constancy

3

One of the assumptions that we rely on in using our senses is that the external world has a degree of constancy, that we can use certain phenomena as standards to compare with new experiences. Let's take the lightness in appearance of an object as an example. As we have seen in Section 2.2, most objects do not emit light themselves, but reflect light from some other source such as the Sun or a fluorescent light. The amount of light reflected depends both on the amount of light striking the surface (its **illumination**) and on the proportion of this light that is reflected (its **reflectance**). Reflectance is independent of the illumination of an object or surface.

Look at Figure 3.1. This shows three arrow shapes, one coloured black, one mid-grey, and the third (as an outline) is white. Suppose that you look at this Figure under bright illumination, say of intensity 500 units (on some arbitrary scale). The black arrow looks black because it only reflects a small proportion of the incident light, say 2 per cent, and this is the light that enters your eye when you 'see' the arrow. The light reflected is therefore of intensity 10 units (2 per cent of 500).

Figure 3.1 Three arrow shapes, one black, one mid-grey and one white.

○ Assume that the white arrow reflects 98 per cent and the mid-grey 50 per cent of the incident light. What is the intensity of the reflected light for each arrow?

● The light reflected from the white arrow will be 490 units (98 per cent of 500) and the mid-grey 250 units (50 per cent of 500).

Suppose now that you took the text outside at twilight, where, for the sake of argument, the incident light intensity is only 50 units. The intensity of reflected light that enters your eye now would be much reduced.

○ What would the reflected light intensity be in each case?

● The black arrow would reflect 1 unit, the mid-grey 25 units, and the white 49 units.

Despite the fact that, outside, the white arrow reflects less light than the mid-grey arrow under bright illumination inside, *you would still see it as white rather than a darker grey*. This phenomenon is called **lightness constancy**. It is the result of the brain using various cues from the objects or surfaces adjacent to the one being examined. The difference is therefore in the perception of lightness.

These standards or constancies can often seemingly be brought into question and our brain fooled into providing misleading interpretations of the signals received by our senses. Such errors of perception are called **illusions**. The majority of illusions are visual, but they can involve the other senses.

Look at the illustration shown in Figure 3.2, which involves a related aspect of lightness that affects our perception of lightness constancy. There are a total of 9 circles, some of which appear to be raised above the surface of the paper and others appear to be hollows.

○ Which come into the first category and which into the second?

● The circles at the four corners and the one in the centre appear to most people to be raised above the surface of the paper, and the rest to be hollows.

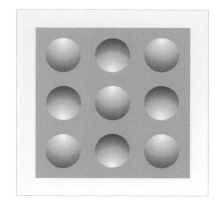

Figure 3.2 A pattern of shaded circles.

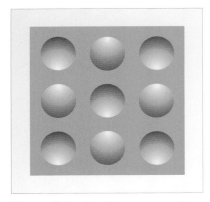

Figure 3.3 Another pattern of shaded circles.

Now look at Figure 3.3 and repeat the exercise.

❍ Now which come into the first category and which into the second?

● It is the exact converse. The circles at the four corners and the one in the centre now appear to most people to be hollows and the rest to be raised above the surface of the paper.

You may be surprised to learn that Figure 3.3 is simply Figure 3.2 but turned upside down. Why should that simple change alter our perception of the circles? Remember, the circles are simply drawings and are in fact only two-dimensional in nature. The eye is therefore only seeing something that is flat. It is the brain that takes that information and by comparing it with the store of accumulated experience interprets the circles as being raised above or hollowed below the paper.

❍ Look at the light and shade portions of each circle, and compare each with the background. Can you guess why the brain interprets the images as it does?

In the vast majority of cases, light comes from above, whether it be the sun or artificial sources of illumination. Hence, using this stored experience, the brain makes that assumption, and those circles where the light part is above the dark part look as they would if actually three-dimensional and lit from above. The dark parts would then be in shadow. In contrast, those circles where the dark part is on top look as they would if hollowed out from a solid surface and lit from above. In each case, the fact that the lighter part of the circle is a lighter colour than the background and the darker part is darker than the background is an essential clue that the brain uses to create the three-dimensional perception.

The presumed effect of the way an object is lit is called a **visual cue**. It provides the brain with a clue that it then uses in creating the overall perception of the picture being looked at. In the above example, the key visual cues used by the brain are fairly obvious. In many other instances, there are several different cues, and an illusion can be created either by removing or changing some important cues or by combining cues that are in conflict with one another. In the latter case, the brain is tricked so that what you perceive depends on how you look at the image.

For hundreds of years, artists have been employing visual cues (called **depth cues**) to create realistic-looking three-dimensional pictures using two-dimensional images. One of the greatest advances in the history of art was the discovery of **perspective** during the Renaissance period. Perspective involves the use of various visual cues to give the correct impression of a three-dimensional scene on a two-dimensional surface. The artist Masaccio together with architect Brunelleschi and the sculptor Donatello, who were his contemporaries in Florence, are generally credited with being key figures in the introduction of correct perspective. The introduction of perspective in Masaccio's paintings took place in an amazingly short period. The difference can readily be seen between a picture he painted in 1422 (Figure 3.4), which looks two-dimensional in character, and one painted just a few years later (Figure 3.5) that explicitly made use of perspective to create a much more realistic scene with real three-dimensional character.

Pictures are by their very nature two-dimensional. A variety of cues are used in order to create an impression of three dimensions. These include interposition, relative height, relative size, and linear perspective. Combinations of these cues create a strong sense of depth in a picture.

Figure 3.4   The triptych *Madonna and Child with Saints c.*1422 by Masaccio (1401–*c.*1428) (panel, San Pietro a Cascia, Reggello).

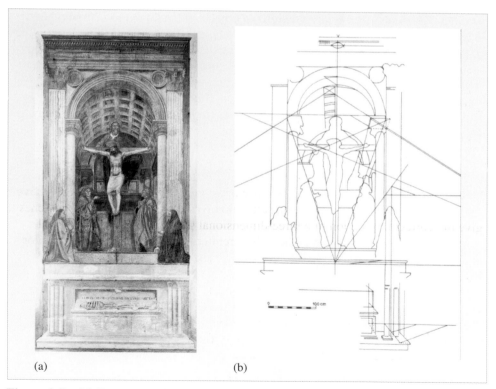

(a)   (b)

Figure 3.5   (a) *Trinity c.* 1425 by Masaccio (fresco, Santa Maria Novella, Florence); (b) the artist's preliminary drawing showing the scheme of the perspective.

Interposition is the blocking of a more distant object by a nearer one. Look at Figure 3.6. The figures shown all look fairly similar in size. What enables you to work out which is closer and which further away is the partial obscuring of an individual figure by another one in front of it. This gives an impression of depth to the picture, though this is not usually very strong when interposition in the sole depth cue present.

Figure 3.6 Some of the 8000 terracotta warriors forming the army guarding the tomb of Qin Shihuang, Emperor from 221 to 210 BC, located near Xi'an in China.

Another depth cue is the **relative height** of objects in a picture (sometimes called **height-in-the-field**). Looking at a picture of a landscape is a good illustration of the effect of relative height in giving a sense of depth. Generally, in such pictures the horizon is near the middle of the picture. Objects on the ground that are near to the viewer are then nearest the bottom of the picture, with ones further away being higher in the picture but still below the horizon. Similarly, flying objects would be near the top of the picture if close to, and lower towards the horizon if further away. Relative height is a powerful depth cue. Figure 3.7 is a good example of relative height with other depth cues being largely absent.

Figure 3.7 Monument Valley, Utah used as a location for numerous western films (most notably those produced by John Ford) and television commercials.

Relative size of similar objects or of people is also a strong depth cue (Figure 3.8). The further away from the observer a person is, the smaller they appear to be. To understand why this is so, you need to have a basic idea of how the eye functions. As we saw in Section 2.2, the initial step in the process of vision is the formation of an image of the object being viewed on the retina at the back of the eye (Figure 3.9). When an object or person is further away, the image formed on the retina is smaller than when they are closer to. This effect gives a strong impression of depth particularly in pictures containing people.

Figure 3.8   A picture showing relative size as a depth cue. The people on the far side of the pool seem to be less than half the size of those on the near side, but are not perceived to be midget-sized. This is even more true of the minuscule figures that you can just see on the beach beyond!

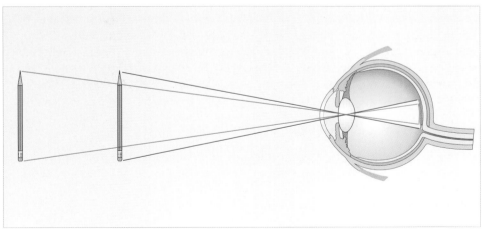

Figure 3.9   A simplified diagram of the human eye showing the relationship between the distance of an object from the eye and the size of the resultant image on the retina.

However, if this were the only factor that affected how we perceive size, as you watched someone (a full-grown adult) walk away from you down the street, they would appear to shrink to the size of a small child. Yet we know that the person remains the same size; the brain processes the information received from the retina concerning the apparent size of the person but taking into account at the same time the apparent size of buildings, vehicles and other objects in the field of vision, together with accumulated experience. This perception that the size of a person, animal or object remains the same irrespective of distance from the observer is another example of a constancy, called **size constancy**.

Perhaps the best known depth cue is **linear perspective**. This is the effect occurring when parallel lines between points that are near and ones further away appear to converge, for example when looking along a railway track or a road. Figure 3.10 shows this type of depth cue.

Figure 3.10 Eurostar passing Wandsworth Road, London.

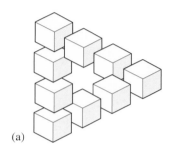

(a)

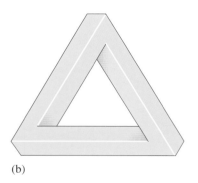

(b)

Figure 3.11 (a) Artist's impression of Oscar Reutersvard's impossible triangle. (b) The impossible triangle devised by Roger and Lionel Penrose.

Visual illusions are caused by the brain interpreting what the eye sees according to preconceived expectations. They arise when certain perspective cues are misinterpreted or inadequate (Box 3.1). One such class of illusions are what is known as '**impossible figures**'. The Swedish artist Oscar Reutersvard was the first to deliberately draw impossible figures, when, in 1934, he created the first impossible triangle by a carefully arranged set of cubes (Figure 3.11a). Some twenty years later, mathematician Roger Penrose, who did not know of Reutersvard's work, attended a lecture by the Dutch graphic artist Maurits Corneille Escher, which inspired him to rediscover the impossible triangle. He created it in its most familiar form (Figure 3.12b), which he published and popularized in a 1958 article, co-authored with his father, biologist Lionel Penrose.

In 1961 Escher, inspired by the Penrose version of the impossible triangle (he was sent a copy of the article by the Penroses) created his famous lithograph 'Waterfall' (Figure 3.12), which makes use of the same conflicting perspective cues by incorporating effectively two impossible triangles linked together.

Activity 3.1 Some further illusions

You should now undertake this DVD activity which will allow you to experience some illusions interactively, and others that involve motion, neither of which can be demonstrated in printed text. Before doing so, read Question 3.2, which you should be able to answer once you have completed the activity. Further instructions are given in the Block 1 Study File.

Box 3.1   Visual illusions and piloting aircraft

One activity where visual illusions can have positively dangerous consequences is piloting an aircraft. The Instrument Flying Handbook issued by the U.S. Federal Aviation Administration observes that 'Of the senses, vision is the most important for safe flight. However, various surface features and atmospheric conditions encountered when landing can create illusions …'. It identifies the five major illusions leading to landing errors to be related to effects of: (a) runway width; (b) runway and terrain slope; (c) featureless terrain; (d) atmospheric conditions; and (e) ground lighting.

Depending on the type of illusion, the effect can be to give the impression that the aircraft is at a higher altitude than it actually is, with the risk of landing short, or have the opposite effect, with the attendant risk of overshooting.

Features that create an illusion of being at higher altitude are: a narrower than usual runway; a runway or surrounding terrain that slopes upwards; the absence of surrounding ground features, such as when flying over water, darkened areas, or snow-covered terrain; rain on the windscreen; or atmospheric haze.

Features that create an illusion of being at lower altitude are: a wider than usual runway, a runway or surrounding terrain that slopes downwards, or a bright runway and approach lights with otherwise dark surroundings.

Other hazards are fog, which can create an illusion of the aircraft climbing, and lights along a road that can be mistaken for runway and approach lights.

Figure 3.12   'Waterfall' by Escher.

Question 3.1

Which depth cues are in conflict in the Penrose impossible triangle?

Question 3.2

Which depth cues are in conflict for the ball and shadow illusion?

3.1 Summary of Section 3

One of the assumptions that we rely on in using our senses is that the external world has a degree of constancy. An example is the perceived relative lightness of a surface which remains essentially the same irrespective of the intensity of its illumination, although the absolute intensity of the light reflected can vary greatly. This is called lightness constancy. When these standards or constancies are seemingly brought into question, the result is an error of perception called an illusion. An example is the use of shading to indicate three-dimensional character in a drawing. This is the result of a visual cue relating to the presumed way in which a real three-dimensional object would be lit.

Other visual cues that help give a picture three-dimensional character are interposition, relative height, relative size, and linear perspective. The use of relative size makes use of another example of constancy, size constancy. When any of the visual cues are in conflict either with itself applied to a different part of the image or a different cue, the result is to produce an illusion, a figure that cannot exist in three-dimensions, such as the Penrose impossible triangle. Illusions can involve senses other than vision, though the majority are visual. Other visual illusions arise from conflicting motion cues.

Question 3.3

Which depth cues can you identify in Figure 3.13?

Figure 3.13   The Grand Union Canal at Stoke Bruerne, Northamptonshire.

Impairment and dysfunction

4.1 Introduction

In the previous section we examined the phenomenon of illusions, whereby the brain creates a false image based on the signals it receives. We now turn to the much more difficult area of impairment and dysfunction. Examples range from the inability to hear certain frequencies (usually the very high or very low) to total deafness; from mild colour blindness (strictly colour deficiency) to total blindness; from localized numbness to the handful of people who have total loss of proprioception or touch; and from the inability to detect various odours or tastes to the very rare total loss of smell or taste. In this section we shall look at one or two for each sense in turn; we shall then discuss them in more detail at various points throughout the course.

4.2 Hearing disorders

Certain people are often said to be 'tone deaf' if they are unable to sing in tune or sometimes even to appreciate music. You should be able to decide for yourself whether this is the result of some abnormality in the ear or is more related to the perception process once you have studied Block 3, which deals with hearing. However, individuals suffering from what might be regarded as more fundamental hearing disorders can be grouped into two classes: those who suffer from partial or total deafness, that is whose ability to hear the full range of sound frequencies is reduced or absent, and those who suffer from an impaired ability to hear certain frequencies, whereas their ability to hear others is unaffected. In this brief introduction to sensory impairment, we shall focus on the latter.

Hearing disorders can arise in a number of ways. We are quite familiar with the fact that in general our hearing becomes less acute with age. Sadly, too, some children are born with hearing impairment. A third, increasingly frequent, cause is the proliferation of discos and clubs where music is played at such high volumes that physical damage to the inner ear may result. However, while the presence of partial deafness across the whole frequency range is not difficult to detect, the selective impairment of particular frequency bands may more easily pass unnoticed. To assess this dependably, the specialist testing equipment used by an audiologist is necessary. However, it is possible to use the sound facilities of a computer to gain a rough measure of one's hearing range, and a qualitative picture of hearing sensitivity across the auditory spectrum.

Activity 4.1 Tests for selective hearing deficiency

You should now undertake this DVD activity which will allow you to check your own hearing range using the computer. Because of the limitations of computer sound systems, it should not be taken to give other than a rough measure. However, if it raises any concerns about your own hearing then please consult your doctor. Further instructions are given in the Block 1 Study File.

STUDY FILE

4.3 Vision disorders

Vision disorders can be divided into two main categories, those that affect the ability to see anything, and those that affect the ability to see particular colours. In this section we shall take a preliminary look at this latter impairment, which is usually called colour blindness but should more correctly be called colour deficiency.

Colour deficiency is a condition that affects about eight per cent of males but a only a few tenths of a percent of females. This means that it must arise from the X chromosome, since if it involved the Y chromosome, females would never be affected. The reason females get it so much less often is because it is a recessive gene on the X-chromosome, and females have two X chromosomes whereas males have only one and the gene, even though recessive, will be expressed. In the majority of cases, females carry a dominant gene on the other X chromosome that masks the effect of the recessive gene.

There are various types of colour deficiency, some more severe than others. As you saw in Section 2.2, the colours seen on a television or computer screen are made up from various combinations of red, blue and green. The relationship between this empirical fact and our ability to see colours will be dealt with in Block 4. That there is an intimate relationship is apparent, however, from the fact that the majority of those suffering from colour blindness have a red-green colour deficiency.

Figure 4.1 is an example of the images used to test for colour deficiency.

❍   Look at Figure 4.1.What number can you can see?

●   Those with normal colour vision should be able to see the number 73; those who suffer from red-green colour deficiencies will not be able to read this number or will read it incorrectly.

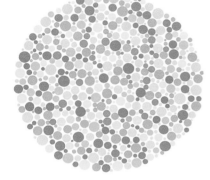

Figure 4.1   An image used to test for colour deficiency of the type devised by the ophthalmologist Shinobu Ishihara at the University of Tokyo and first published in 1917.

Broadly, there are three categories of people with abnormal colour vision called anomalous-trichromats, dichromats, and monochromats. Anomalous trichromats can detect the full spectrum of colours, but their spectral sensitivity profiles are significantly different from that of normal trichromats, and as a consequence, when matching colours produce quite different results from those of a normal trichromat. Dichromats are deficient in one of these three primary colours, and perceive the deficient colour as grey. Monochromats are deficient in two of the primary colours.

Activity 4.2   Tests for colour deficiency

You should now undertake this DVD activity which will allow you to do a rough check of your own colour vision using the computer. This test, which is quite straightforward, will allow you to confirm the nature of any colour deficiency. If you have a colour deficiency, you are almost certainly aware of it already. However, if it raises any concerns about your own colour vision then please consult your doctor. Further instructions are given in the Block I Study File.

4.4 Touch and pain disorders

While we are all too familiar with vision and hearing impairment, it is much less common to come across people who have disorders involving their sense of touch or of pain. While these might seem less debilitating than those involving sight or hearing, in fact they can be at least as severe. Pain is a complex and unpleasant experience signalling tissue damage. The capacity to respond quickly to such damage is vital to the survival of the individual, and is one of the most important functions of the sense of pain. If the ability to feel pain is absent, the body is at risk of permanent damage since there is no perception of the signal indicating the need to take swift action. For example, such an individual would not know that they were sustaining severe burns when touching a hotplate, except possibly when their sense of smell told them.

One well-known case reported by D. W. Baxter and J. Olszewski, two doctors working in Canada, involved a young female who did not experience pain. During her childhood she suffered many cuts, burns, bruises, frostbite and even abscesses without any pain. As a consequence she was hospitalized on three occasions by the age of eight. By then, she was old enough to realize that she was unusual in lacking sensitivity to pain, and was able to take precautions to avoid any serious injuries. When she was aged 22, she underwent a series of neurological tests that confirmed her total lack of pain perception when her hand was immersed in hot water long enough to cause skin blistering, nor did she exhibit any of the normally associated physiological changes such as increases in pulse rate or blood pressure. Soon after, she began to experience severe orthopaedic problems. By the age of 23 she was limping badly and investigation showed substantial pathological changes to her hip joints and spine. This was put down to lack of pain sensations so that she was not alerted to change her posture and consequently caused severe inflammation of the joints. The patient died at the age of 29 as a result of incurable infections of the hip.

Cases such as this one where the lack of sensation is present from birth (congenital) are, fortunately, very rare. Much more common is the loss of sensation through disease. The most common cause world-wide of the loss of both touch and pain sensation is leprosy (also known as Hansen's disease). It is most common in those parts of the world that are warm and wet, in the tropics and subtropics. Despite a campaign to eradicate the disease, at the time of writing more than 700 000 new cases a year are still being detected (Figure 4.2).

1.0-1.9

2.0-6.0

Figure 4.2 World Health Organization map of leprosy prevalence in 2000 given in cases per 10 000 population: orange 1.0–1.9; red 2.0–6.0.

Figure 4.3   The hand of a leprosy patient that has been severely burned as a result of profound loss of sensation.

Leprosy is caused by a bacterium (*Mycobacterium leprae*) which attacks the peripheral nerves and the skin. Bacterial growth occurs preferentially in the extremities, leading to partial or total loss of sensation resulting from damage to the peripheral nervous system (**polyneuropathy**; see Figure 4.3). Unfortunately, the nerve damage caused by leprosy is permanent. This means that even when cured by the use of multidrug therapy with three different antibiotics, dapsone, rifampicin and clofazimine, the most effective treatment regime, many people infected by leprosy for a significant length of time will suffer from a loss of sensation for the rest of their life. Consequently, they need to be constantly on guard against even minor injuries such as cuts and burns that can lead to infections and other complications if not treated.

Leprosy is extremely rare in the developed world, where diabetes is the most common cause of the loss of touch and pain sensation. One estimate puts the number of people in the United States and Europe who suffer from diabetes-related polyneuropathy at more than 17 million. The causes of peripheral nerve damage suffered by diabetics are not yet fully understood, but are the result of elevated blood glucose levels. Curiously, it is characterized not just by the loss of sensation mainly in the feet and legs but also, somewhat paradoxically, by pain in the same locations. The dangers are similar to those suffered by those who contract leprosy, and if wounds to the feet are not treated, they may become ulcerated and eventually this may mean that the foot has to be amputated.

4.5 Smell and taste disorders

The occurrence of smell and state disorders is more common than many people suppose. The total absence of the sense of smell is called **anosmia** and the absence of the sense of taste is **ageusia**; impaired senses of smell or taste are called **hyposmia** and **hypogeusia** respectively. Although seemingly less problematic than vision and hearing disorders, none the less these disorders can have a substantial impact on an individual's quality of life. For example, it can affect an individual's choice of food, and lead to an increased intake of sugar or salt to compensate, both of which can have adverse health effects. It can even lead to malnutrition, especially for the elderly for whom smell and taste dysfunction is more common. Our sense of smell also acts as an early warning system: it alerts us to the presence of gas leaks, poisonous fumes and even fires, and enables us to detect food and beverages that are spoiled or have gone bad, so avoiding the constant risk of food poisoning.

A few people are born with a faulty sense of smell or taste (they rarely occur together), but for most people who suffer from chemosensory dysfunction it develops as a result of injury or illness. The noticeable loss of the sense of smell or taste may in fact be the first symptom of an illness, and so lead to earlier diagnosis and hence treatment than might otherwise be the case. For example, recent research has shown that a loss of the sense of smell can act as an early warning system for the onset of Alzheimer's disease. Overall, smell disorders are more common than taste disorders. Table 4.1 gives some possible causes of smell disorders, and Table 4.2 gives some possible causes of taste disorders.

The most common cause of smell and taste dysfunction is ageing, with loss of smell being much more frequent than loss of taste. Most people's sense of smell is most acute between the ages of 30 and 60. After age 60, progressive loss of the sense of smell sets in, so that in the age group 65–80, half have moderate to severe smell loss, and above age 80, seventy-five per cent have moderate to severe loss of smell.

Table 4.1   Selected possible causes of smell disorders.*

Common causes	Less common causes	Uncommon causes
nasal and sinus disease	medications	neoplasm or brain tumour
upper respiratory infection	cocaine abuse (intranasal)	psychiatric conditions
head trauma (e.g. frontal skull fracture)	toxic chemical exposure	endocrine disorders
cigarette smoking	industrial agent exposure	epilepsy
neurodegenerative disease (e.g. Alzheimer's disease, Parkinson's disease, multiple sclerosis)	nutritional factors (e.g. vitamin deficiency)	migraine headache
	radiation treatment of head and neck	cerebrovascular accident
age	congenital conditions	systemic lupus erythematosus

*Source: 'Smell and taste disorders: a primary care approach' by Steven M. Bromley, *American Family Physician*, 15 January, 2000.

Table 4.2   Selected possible causes of taste disorders.*

Common causes	Less common causes	Uncommon causes
oral infections	nutritional factors (e.g. vitamin deficiency)	psychiatric conditions
Bell's palsy		epilepsy
medications	tumour or lesions associated with taste pathways	migraine headache
oral appliances (e.g. dentures, filling materials, tooth prosthetics)	head trauma	Sjögren's syndrome
		multiple sclerosis
dental procedures	toxic chemical exposure	endocrine disorders
	industrial agent exposure	
age	radiation treatment of head and neck	

*Source: 'Smell and taste disorders: a primary care approach' by Steven M. Bromley, *American Family Physician*, 15 January, 2000.

Initially, it might seem that it is much more difficult to determine if a person has a chemosensory disorder, and its extent, than say disorders of vision or hearing where the signals are much more easily controlled and the response seems generally to be less subjective. However, there are techniques that can be used quite reproducibly. For smell, it involves finding out the lowest concentration of the test substance that the patient can detect. The test can also involve a comparison of the odours of different substances or a determination of the relationship between the concentration of the test chemical and the perceived strength of its smell. This can now easily be achieved following the development of a 'scratch-and-sniff' test kit by scientists at the University of Pennsylvania Smell and Taste Center. This involves scratching a test card impregnated with different substances, and the subject being asked to identify the odour of each given a list of possible substances.

To test the sense of taste, the subject is asked to use what is often called a 'sip, spit, and rinse' test to evaluate the taste of different concentrations of the test substances. Sometimes this involves applying the chemicals being tested directly to specific areas of the tongue. An alternative approach does not require tasting as such, but involves an electrical test using an instrument called an electrogustometer. A probe is used to apply a stimulus at various locations on the tongue and with different intensities, and the response is then measured electrically.

4.6 Summary of Section 4

Some individuals suffer impairment and dysfunction of their sensory system to various extents. Examples range from the inability to hear certain frequencies to total deafness; from mild colour deficiency to total blindness; from localized numbness to total loss of proprioception or touch; and from the inability to detect various odours or tastes, to the very rare total loss of smell or taste.

While partial or total deafness across the entire frequency range is easily recognized, the selective impairment of particular frequency bands may more easily pass unnoticed. To assess this dependably, specialist testing equipment is necessary, but it is possible to use the sound facilities of a computer to gain a rough measure of one's hearing range, and a qualitative picture of hearing sensitivity across the auditory spectrum.

There are various types of colour deficiency, and these can be diagnosed using images of the kind devised by ophthalmologist Shinobu Ishihara or by using colour comparison charts. Broadly, there are three categories of people with abnormal colour vision called anomalous-trichromats, dichromats, and monochromats, depending on the extent to which they are deficient in seeing one or more of the primary colours red, green and blue.

People who have disorders involving their sense of touch or of pain are very rare. Lack of the sense of pain can lead to permanent damage since, if pain is absent, there is no early warning signal that the body is at risk. One individual with congenital universal insensitivity to pain died at the early age of 29 from damage resulting from this lack. Leprosy sufferers and to a lesser extent diabetics are prone to the same problems, because of loss of sensation in the extremities resulting from these diseases.

Smell and taste disorders, though seemingly less problematic than disorders with the other senses, can have a substantial effect on the quality of life. They can affect the diet, as well as introduce dangers caused by the inability to detect gas or smoke or spoiled food. The noticeable loss of the sense of smell or taste may be the first indication of an illness, leading to earlier diagnosis and treatment than might otherwise be the case, for example the early warning of the onset of Alzheimer's disease. The most common cause of smell and taste dysfunction is ageing, but there are many other possible causes. The sense of smell can readily be tested using a 'scratch-and-sniff' test kit developed by scientists at the University of Pennsylvania, and the sense of taste can be tested using a 'sip, spit, and rinse' method. An alternative approach involves using an instrument called an electrogustometer.

Question 4.1

Attempt to frame two or three *general* questions that the above description raises in your mind about impairment or dysfunction of any of the senses. Then compare yours with the questions given in the answer section at the end of the block.

How far can the brain compensate for impairment of any senses? Does this ability change with age?

5

From signal to perception

The study of how our senses work necessitates an interdisciplinary approach. In order to properly understand the whole sequence from signal to perception, we need to be familiar with concepts and ideas from several of the traditional scientific disciplines. Clearly, since it involves the study of living organisms, ourselves, then biology plays a central part. Similarly, much of the process of perception lies within the realm of psychology. However, an understanding of key aspects of physics and chemistry are also required. For example, in order to understand how vision works, we need to know about the nature of light, and how it is transmitted to the receptor cells of the eye (physics). The interaction of light with these receptors, and the transport of neural signals to the brain involves a series of processes at the molecular level and so requires an understanding of how ions and molecules behave (chemistry). Similarly, we need to understand the basics of mechanical, gravitational and inertial forces to learn about touch and the orientation and position of the body in space (physics). A final example is the need for a basic knowledge of the behaviour of molecules (chemistry) to understand taste and smell, often called the chemical senses, as we have seen.

An area where the application of techniques from physics has had a major impact is in the non-invasive imaging of the brain. The imaging techniques used to study the human brain fall into two categories. Structural imaging techniques are used to detect any changes to the form of the brain, for example the growth of a tumour. Functional imaging techniques are used to find out which areas of the brain perform a particular function and to study the sequence of activation of those areas while this is taking place.

Three of the techniques used for this latter purpose are **positron emission tomography** (**PET**), **functional magnetic resonance imaging** (**fMRI**) and **magnetoencephalography** (**MEG**). You will learn more about how these techniques work and what information they can provide later in the course, beginning in Block 2. For now it is sufficient to understand that they use different physical properties to obtain images that show changes produced by any activity of the brain.

Figure 5.1 shows an image of a brain obtained using PET. In this case, the subject was asked to look at words in a book, then to listen to the same words being spoken, and finally to think about these identical words. This illustrates quite clearly that these three activities differ greatly in terms of brain activity although they are

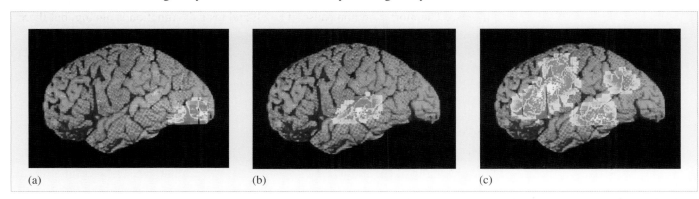

(a)   (b)   (c)

Figure 5.1   PET image of the brain while (a) looking at words, (b) listening to words and (c) thinking of words.

apparently similar, namely the words in question are being imprinted on the subject's consciousness. Clearly looking at the words (Figure 5.1a) entails vision, and would be expected to involve the part of the brain that normally processes the visual signal (Figure 5.2). Similarly, listening to the words (Figure 5.1b) entails hearing, and so would be expected to involve the area of the brain that normally processes the auditory signal. What is so interesting is that thinking about the same words (Figure 5.1c) involves so many other areas of the brain.

Figure 5.2 The areas of the brain normally associated with vision, hearing and touch.

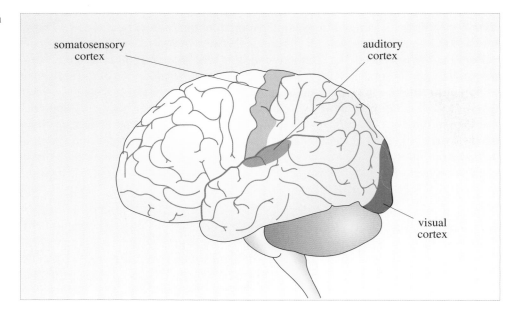

Functional imaging has been used to demonstrate the extent to which the brain can reorganize following changes to the sensory organs. For example, consider the sense of touch. As you will learn later in the course, particular areas of the body map onto different areas of the brain. Thus, normally, touching the tips of the four fingers and thumb gives rise to brain activity in adjacent areas of the somatosensory cortex (Figure 5.2). However, for people born with deformities of the hand, this mapping is very different.

There are many types of congenital hand deformity, one of the most common being syndactyly, or joined fingers. Where possible, it is recommended that surgery to separate the fingers is carried out at as young an age as possible. However, sometimes surgery is not carried out until adulthood. One adult male with congenital syndactyly in which the digits were severely malformed was studied using MEG before and after surgery to separate his connected fingers. Figure 5.3a is an MEG image of his brain that shows an abnormal cortical representation of the digits, with the thumb and little finger very close together. As you will learn later in the course, these are normally well separated, with the representation of the other fingers in between. Figure 5.3b shows an MEG image of the same area of the brain taken 26 days after surgical separation of his fingers. Now, the representation of the thumb and little finger are well separated, with the other digits in between.

Images such as those shown in Figures 5.1 and 5.3, only routinely available since the beginning of the 1990s, have transformed research into the science of the senses, and now provide for each type of sensation an almost direct view of the link between the signal and the resulting perception of the overall sensory experience.

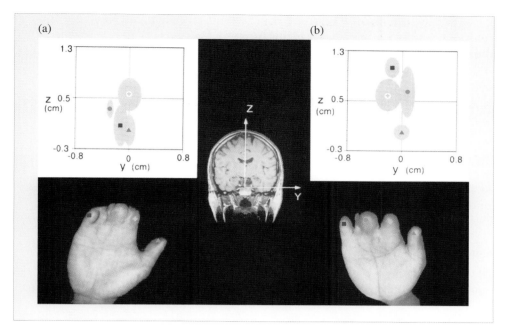

Figure 5.3   (a) A map of the cortical representation in the coronal plane of the digits of the right hand of an adult male with congenital syndactyly obtained using MEG. The coloured symbols indicate which digit corresponds to which area of the brain; (b) a map of the same area obtained 26 days after surgery to separate the fingers.

Before the development of functional imaging techniques, research into which areas of the brain were involved with the functioning of each of the senses relied on empirical investigations carried out on cadavers and on living subjects during brain surgery. Throughout the cortex there are visually apparent differences in cell anatomy which can be used to define and differentiate areas of the cerebral cortex. In the early twentieth century, the famous German neuroscientist Korbinian Brodmann carried out a seminal study in which he divided the cortex into 47 different numbered zones or areas (**Brodmann's areas**) each with its own distinctive anatomy (Figure 5.4). What Brodmann suspected, but was unable to prove with the techniques available to him, was that the different zones he identified performed different functions. Subsequently, the use of sophisticated stimulation and recording methods, and more recently functional imaging techniques such as fMRI and PET,

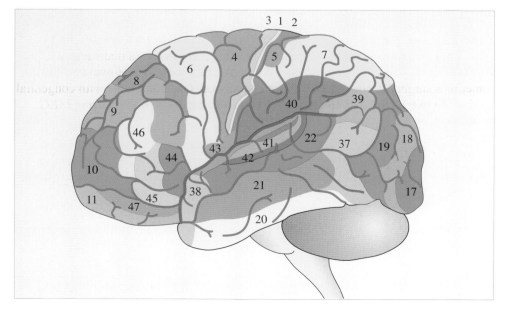

Figure 5.4   Some of the 47 zones or areas identified by Korbinian Brodmann.

have revealed that many of these areas are indeed associated with particular functions. For example, area 4 is motor cortex, associated with the contraction of muscles, and area 17 is visual cortex, which receives the input from the eye. Though originally simply delineated by appearance, for ease and consistency of communication, neuroscientists often still refer to the different parts of the cortex according to Brodmann's classification, and you will meet this nomenclature at a number of points through the course.

We have now reached the end of Block 1. It has had the overall aim of introducing the subject of the human senses and to start you thinking about the questions that we hope to answer in the rest of the course. As you will see, the ways in which information is transmitted from the signal receptors to the brain for all the various senses have much in common. In Block 2 we shall examine this common mechanism in some detail.

Question 5.1

About one person in 2000 experiences the phenomenon of synaesthesia, that is they experience more than one sensory perception associated with a given stimulus. For example, some people see music in terms of colours, 'feel' tastes or 'smell' sounds. Suggest one possible method of investigation to determine whether a given individual experiences genuine synaesthesia or if it is simply the product of an active imagination.

5.1 Summary of Section 5

The study of the human senses necessitates an interdisciplinary approach. In order to properly understand the whole sequence from signal to perception, we need to be familiar with concepts and ideas not just from biology and psychology, but also from physics and chemistry.

One area where the application of techniques from physics has had a major impact is in the non-invasive imaging of the brain. Imaging techniques used to study the human brain fall into two categories: structural imaging techniques (used to detect any changes to the form of the brain) and functional imaging techniques (used to study the areas of the brain that perform a particular function). Three of the techniques used for this latter purpose are positron emission tomography (PET), functional magnetic resonance imaging (fMRI) and magnetoencephalography (MEG). Examples of their use are to obtain PET images of the brain while subjects are looking at, listening to, and thinking of words, and MEG imaging of the somatosensory cortex of patients with joined fingers prior to and following separation.

Before the development of functional imaging techniques, neuroscientists relied on empirical investigations to delineate the different areas of the brain. The German neuroscientist Korbinian Brodmann divided the cortex into 47 different numbered zones or areas based on their individual distinctive anatomy. For ease and consistency of communication, neuroscientists still refer to the different parts of the cortex according to Brodmann's classification.

Objectives for Block I

Now that you have completed this block, you should be able to:

1   Define and use, or recognize definitions and applications of, each of the terms printed in **bold** in the text. (*Questions 2.2, 2.7, 2.9 and 2.11*)

2   Describe the initial stages of sensation for each of the senses of hearing, vision, touch, pain, smell and taste. (*Question 2.13*)

3   Distinguish between sensation and perception. (*Questions 1.2, 1.3 and 2.3*)

4   (a) Identify the use of interposition, relative height, and linear perspective as depth cues in two-dimensional pictures of three-dimensional scenes; (b) give examples of visual cues in depth perception. (*Question 3.3*)

5   Analyse and explain visual illusions by identifying the visual cues behind the illusion. (*Questions 3.1 and 3.2*)

6   Use the correct anatomical terms to describe relative directions and positions within the brain and the rest of the human body. (*Question 1.1*)

7   (a) Give examples of the use of functional imaging in studying the senses; (b) suggest how its application could provide information of use in studying aspects of the human sensory system. (*Question 5.1*)

8   Carry out and interpret simple hearing and vision tests to study the relationship between physical stimuli and the resulting perception. (*Questions 2.1, 2.5, 2.6, 3.1 and 3.2*)

9   Combine information provided about aspects of the human senses with previous knowledge to formulate questions that relate to the functioning of the sensory system. (Questions *2.4, 2.8, 2.10, 2.12 and 4.1*)

Answers to questions

Question 1.1

(a) False. The nose is situated on the medial plane, and the two eyes lie laterally to the left and to the right.

(b) True. Above the neck the terms rostral and caudal mean essentially 'front' and 'back' Clearly, the cerebellum is further back than the frontal lobe.

(c) True. The term contralateral means 'on opposite sides of the medial plane'.

(d) False. The parietal lobe is above the temporal lobe, not in front of it. The correct description would be that the parietal lobe is dorsal (or superior) to the temporal lobe.

(e) True. Below the neck, rostral means the upper part of the body and caudal means the lower part. The spinal cord lies in a vertical direction.

(f) True. The medial plane lies in the centre along the left-right direction, and the spinal cord lies centrally and at the rear in a front-back direction.

Question 1.2

Sensation is the process in which various stimuli interact with receptors in our sense organs giving rise to electrical signals that are then carried by the nervous system to the brain. Perception is the process by which this sensory information is assembled, combined with information retrieved from our memory, and interpreted in the brain.

Question 1.3

One example is the eventual perception of a DNA double helix in Figure 1.9 when the initial image is just of a complex geometric pattern. The other example is the perception of a subjective square lying on top of four complete solid circles in Figure 1.10b, while no such perception is apparent when the same component shapes are arranged differently as in Figure 1.10a.

Question 2.1

The degree of sensitivity to frequency changes depends on a large number of factors including the frequency of the notes used, and varies greatly from person to person, for example it is affected by musical training. As a rough guide, the best that can be achieved is about 3 Hz for tones of frequency around 100 Hz (3%), about 5 Hz for tones of 1000 Hz (1 kHz) (0.5%), and about 100 Hz for tones around 10 kHz (1%).

Question 2.2

(a) True. Tones with more complex waveforms, like those shown in Figure 2.7, can be analysed to give a fundamental and one or more overtones with the shape of a sine wave. You will learn more about this in Block 3.

(b) False. This is the frequency of the second overtone or third harmonic (remember the fundamental is the first harmonic). The first overtone of a 300 Hz fundamental, which is the second harmonic, is 600 Hz (2×300), and the second overtone or third harmonic is 900 Hz (3×300).

(c) False. At a constant temperature and pressure, the speed of sound in air has a fixed value. High frequency tones have a shorter wavelength than low frequency ones, but travel at the same speed.

(d) True. The notes with frequencies of 262 Hz and 294 Hz have a ratio of 1:1.12, whereas the two notes with frequencies of 262 Hz and 330 Hz have a ratio of 1:1.26 (very close to $4:5$; the actual frequencies are not exact whole numbers). Hence the latter would be expected to sound more pleasant. On a keyboard (see Figure 2.5) 262 Hz corresponds to middle C, 294 Hz to the note D to the right, and 330 Hz to the note E to the right of that.

Question 2.3

The stereo effect is due to a combination of both signal and perception. In general, the array of sound reaching the ears is not laterally symmetrical, so the composition of the sound signal reaching the left ear will differ from that reaching the right ear. However, the two will have much in common, and the brain has to disentangle the information that indicates the spatial arrangement of the sound sources from that which is common to both ears, a function that is most definitely part of the perceptual process.

Question 2.4

This is the first of a number of similar questions relating to the various senses. Obviously with an open question such as this, you may well have come up with quite different questions, which is not to say that they are any the less valid. It is simply that in the rest of the course we shall be attempting to answer the questions listed below, among others.

1 What is the role of the various components of the ear?

2 How does the cochlea convert the energy in sound waves to electrical signals?

3 Do all sound frequencies follow the same route to the brain?

4 How is the source of a sound located in space?

5 What are the causes of deafness?

6 Can loud sounds permanently damage your hearing?

Question 2.5

The smallest perceptible difference in colour depends on whether you are changing the amount of a primary at low intensities or at high intensities. Starting with pure red (i.e. R = 255, G = 0, B = 0), and progressively adding green, a perceptible difference only becomes apparent when the G value reaches 60 or more. However, if you start off with yellow (R = 255, G = 255, B = 0), it is possible to detect a decrease of only 4 in the G value. Obviously, if you are colour deficient to any extent, this will probably affect the result you get carrying out this activity.

Question 2.6

It is very unlikely that you would notice the difference. Given the answer to the previous question, most people cannot detect any difference when the amount of any primary is changed by just one step out of 256. Consequently, at best, the 256 levels are effectively reduced to 128, and so 128 different levels of each primary colour would give the same number of perceptible colours as 256.

Question 2.7

(a) True. Looking at Figure 2.11, green has a wavelength around 515–545 nm, whereas yellow has a wavelength range of approximately 570–590 nm.

(b) False. From Figure 2.13, magenta is the complementary colour of green, and yellow is the complementary colour of blue.

(c) True. On a computer with 256 levels of each primary colour, the lower the number in the range 0–255, the darker the colour (a mixture with R = 0, G = 0 and B = 0 gives black).

(d) False. Colour printers make use of subtractive colours, and from Figure 2.15, blue is produced by a mixture of magenta and cyan. Colour printers do not use green ink.

Question 2.8

As with Question 2.4, you may well have come up with quite different, but none the less valid, questions about colour vision. Those listed below are ones that we shall be attempting to answer in the rest of the course.

1 Does the fact that we can create any colour by mixing various proportions of three primary colours mean that the eye has different receptors for the three colours?

2 If the answer to the previous question is yes, do they correspond to the additive primaries or the subtractive primaries?

3 How does the retina convert the energy in light waves to electrical signals?

4 Why can we only see objects in shades of grey on a dark night?

5 How is the information about colour processed by the brain?

6 What are the causes of colour blindness?

Question 2.9

(a) False. It is the higher density of receptors rather than their proximity to the surface of the skin that results in the fingertips being more sensitive than the back of the hand.

(b) False. The two symbols are identical, and must therefore be differentiated in some other way. The most likely is that a question mark always comes at the end of a sentence, whereas an opening quotation mark will always have a space before it.

(c) True. The expectation of pain relief may be sufficient to trigger the release of endorphins, which then provide pain relief, despite the lack of any external medication.

(d) True. Peptides are fragments of proteins, so must have a similar composition in terms of the monomer units.

Question 2.10

As with previous questions, you may well have come up with quite different, but none the less valid, questions about the somatic sensory system. Those listed below are ones that we shall be attempting to answer in the rest of the course.

1 How do the various receptor cells differ for the different somatic sensory modalities: touch, pain, proprioception, kinesthesis, and temperature?

2 Why does the greater density of touch receptors result in greater sensitivity?

3 What is the role of the endorphins?

4 What is the cause of phantom pain?

5 How is pain suppressed under certain circumstances?

6 What are the mechanisms of the various methods of pain management, and how do they compare in terms of their effectiveness?

Question 2.11

(a) True. Wood is not volatile of itself, and so cannot stimulate the olfactory receptors. It must be due to some volatile constituent, namely the sap, a conclusion supported by the fact that the smell fades with time as the wood dries out.

(b) False. The shape of a molecule has a major determining effect on the odour of a substance, so such a spray should have the desired affect. Indeed this is one means by which certain deodorizing sprays work, although they usually have other effects as well (e.g. they often contain a perfume to mask any residual bad smells).

(c) False. Adaptation is the change in the perception of a sensory experience with time while the stimulus is unchanged. The effect of salt is a more complex one that you will be better able to understand after studying Block 6.

(d) True. Both the taste receptors and the opiate receptors are particular regions of specialized protein molecules that work by interaction of the receptor site with the relevant molecule (the substance being tasted or the endorphin), whereas the touch receptor is a mechanoreceptor that responds to pressure.

Question 2.12

As with previous questions, you may well have come up with quite different, but none the less valid, questions about the smell and taste. Those listed below are ones that we shall be attempting to answer in the rest of the course.

1 What molecular properties determine the smell or taste of a substance?

2 How does the interaction of a molecule with a smell or taste receptor give rise to an electrical signal?

3 What is known about the structures of smell and taste receptors?

4 Why are smell and taste particularly prone to adaptation?

5 Why is the sense of taste so dependent on the sense of smell?

6 Do human pheromones exist?

Question 2.13

In hearing, the stimulus is a sound wave that impinges on the eardrum causing it to vibrate. The vibrations are transmitted via a complex mechanism to the cochlea in the inner ear where the receptors are located. This is where the signal is transformed into a receptor potential, which gives rise to action potentials that are transmitted to the brain. In the sense of smell, the stimulus consists of molecules of the odorant, and these interact with a receptor in the upper nasal cavity. However, the result is similar to hearing in that activating the receptor also gives rise to electrical signals.

Question 3.1

The Penrose impossible triangle does not make use of relative height, relative size or linear perspective. This only leaves interposition, and it is this that causes the conflicts. At each individual vertex, the three-dimensional nature of the drawing is such that one leg is in front of the other. The conflict arises because of the incompatibility of the directions when all three are in the same figure. For example, the top vertex of the triangle has the leg joined to the vertex at the bottom left in front of the one joined to the vertex at the bottom right. The effect on going from top to bottom is therefore for the former apparently to be coming towards you and the latter going away. But the drawing of the vertex at bottom left shows the horizontal leg in front of the leg coming from the top vertex. This is incompatible with the vertex at bottom right being further away than the top vertex, as implied by the drawing for the top vertex.

Question 3.2

This is the relative height or height-in-the-field cue. The motion of the ball remains the same, it is just the movement of the shadow that changes and which therefore gives rise to the different perceptions. When the shadow moves diagonally it matches the motion of the ball and so it looks as though the ball is rolling along the chequer-board. However, when the shadow moves horizontally while the ball moves diagonally, the chequer-board is perceived to be the 'floor' and so it looks as though the ball is rising, rather than rolling. A combination of the two makes the ball appear to bounce.

Question 3.3

There are many examples of interposition, for example the bushy tree just right of centre, the bar attached to the lock gate in front of the person on the extreme right, and the barges in front of the rear lock gate. Relative height and relative size are both present in, for example, the two people opening the lock gate compared with the people further in the distance. And finally, the sides of the lock provide a linear perspective cue. There may well be other examples of these cues that you notice.

Question 4.1

As with previous questions, you may well have come up with quite different, but none the less valid, general questions about sensory impairment or dysfunction. (There are of course many specific questions possible about each individual sense.) Those listed below are ones that we shall be attempting to answer at least partially in the rest of the course.

1 Is there a deficiency in the activation of the receptor by the stimulus?

2 Is there a partial or complete inability of the receptor to effect transduction of the stimulus to produce a receptor potential?

3 Is there damage to the part of peripheral nervous system that is involved with the particular sensory modality that interferes with information reaching the brain?

4 Is there some defect in the relevant area of the brain that interferes with the processing of the incoming signal?

Question 5.1

Perhaps the most obvious method is to use one of the techniques of functional imaging, such as fMRI, PET or MEG. If the subject experiences genuine synaesthesia, then they should exhibit abnormal brain activity, and in particular the areas associated with the additional sensory perception should show activity where normally there would be very little. A less 'high tech' approach would be to test the subject on different occasions separated by (say) a month. If the experience is genuine, then they should be reproducible, for example associating the same colours with particular sounds or musical passages. If, on the other hand, it is imagined, it is much more likely that the sum total of responses will differ significantly.

BLOCK TWO

THE SENSORY NERVOUS SYSTEM

Contents

Introduction

1

In this block we take a reductionist approach to the study of the human nervous system by looking at basic anatomy and underlying biological mechanisms. However, it is important to keep in mind that we are not passive receivers of external stimuli. Our perception of the environment is affected by the way we interact with it. So, although we will describe how a signal impinges upon a sensory receptor, which transfers information along a particular pathway to the brain, it is important to be aware that we exert some control over this process. A moment's thought reveals that we live out our lives in a world that is buzzing with activity. Our sense organs gather more information than we can use and a logical approach to receiving too much information would be to prioritize input and discard irrelevant information. This is exactly what happens.

The filtering of information gathered by the sensory receptors may take place locally, within the sense organ, or it may occur in the nervous system. These are not two mutually exclusive possibilities. The structure or neurophysiology of a sense organ may be such that it responds more strongly to certain kinds of sensory inputs than to others. Indeed, it may not be capable of responding over the full range of a sensory modality. Take for example our sense of hearing. We know from physical measurements that there are many sounds being generated in the environment for which we have no receptive apparatus.

○ Can you give an example of sound that we know to exist but cannot hear?

● A dog whistle uses ultrasound, which is sound of a higher frequency than we can detect.

Our ears are limited to a maximum range of 20 Hz to 20 kHz, but have greatest sensitivity over a range of frequencies from around 200 Hz to 5 kHz and this matches the frequency band wherein lies most of the acoustic power generated by the human voice. Here we have a signal – that produced by the human voice – for which there is an exquisitely designed organ, the ear. In Block 3 you will discover that the ear contains sensory receptors, with an anatomy and physiology that give rise to particular acoustic properties. These properties have allowed the development of a sophisticated communication system.

Similarly, we see light only between red and violet on the electromagnetic spectrum (although babies can see ultraviolet). In Block 4 you will learn that the human eye contains about 120 million light receptors, each capable of discriminating between at least ten levels (orders of magnitude) of light intensity. It is inconceivable that a central processor could make any sense of a simultaneous input from each of the 120 million receptors. So we would postulate that there must be further filtering. Certain kinds of analysis of information take place in the eyes. The eye 'tells' the brain what it sees, preferentially passing on particular information, such as the presence of a large, looming object that forms a rapidly expanding image on the retina (Figure 1.1 overleaf).

○ Why might such an object be significant?

● In general, a moving object represents a change in the environment. A looming object is one that is approaching you and might require a rapid response, be it a car, falling tree, predator, your partner or your boss.

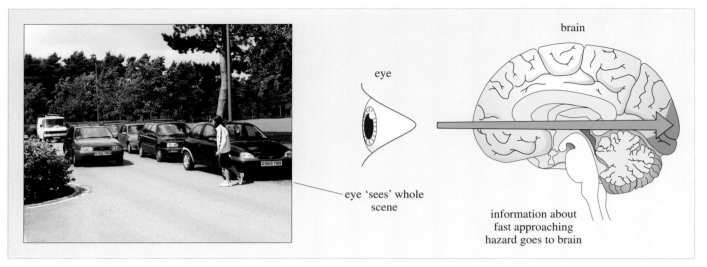

Figure 1.1   The 'eye to brain' reaction to an approaching object.

Incidentally, we do, in general, have particularly good mechanisms for sensing changes in our environment. This makes functional sense, for it is changes that inform us of new threats and new opportunities to which we may wish to react rapidly.

The other way in which information can be filtered or sifted is by processing within the central nervous system. One method is to send different types of information to different places. Look at Figure 5.1 in Block 1. As you look, the information about the colour of the active brain regions is being analysed in your visual cortex and the information about the position of the active brain regions within the whole picture that makes up the visual field is being analysed in your tectum. In other words, two distinct and different regions of the brain are simultaneously analysing different aspects of the visual scene (Figure 1.2). The ability of the brain to take a single stimulus event and to analyse several different aspects of it simultaneously is known as **parallel processing**, and it is a feature of all sensory systems, and indeed all mental activity.

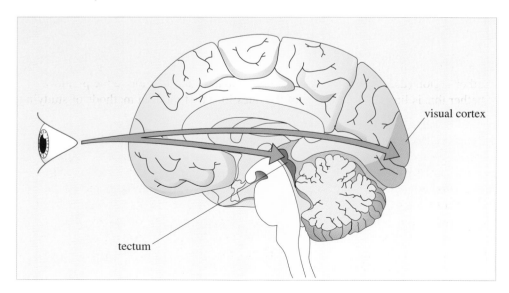

Figure 1.2   The two regions of the brain that simultaneously analyse different aspects of visual information.

A third possibility is that the output from yet another brain region could exert control over incoming signals before they ever reach the brain. Probably the best known example where this is believed to occur is in the suppression of pain during extreme physical exertion in sporting events, or by soldiers injured in battle (for example see Figure 1.3). But what of the situation where you are totally engrossed in your book and you do not hear someone talking to you? Did the information reach your brain or was it suppressed somewhere en route? Brain imaging techniques are beginning to help us to make sense of some of these perceptual puzzles and we shall describe some of these techniques in more detail in Section 4.

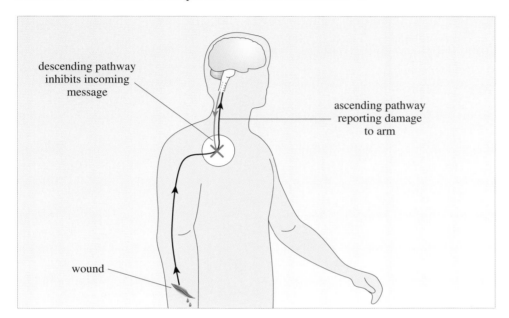

descending pathway
inhibits incoming
message

ascending pathway
reporting damage
to arm

wound

Figure 1.3   The suppression of pain following injury. The descending neural pathway from the brain blocks the incoming neural signals that register tissue damage.

But our perception of a scene remains a unitary experience. The process is further complicated in that our perception of the information is not a passive process, it is an active one. The activity associated with trying to make sense of an image such as Figure 5.1 in Block 1 and putting this new information into a meaningful context is taking place in yet other regions of the brain. It is very different from the process that might occur if another person who was not studying this course looked at the figure whilst hungry and wondering what to eat for dinner. It would seem that one region of the brain (the one that is concerned with hunger) is suppressing activity in another region (the one that is trying to contextualize and memorize the picture). Whether this is literally true is one of the questions that modern methods of studying the brain using functional imaging techniques will allow us to explore.

Although we will be describing signals from one sensory modality at a time, the perception of a signal is modulated by other inputs. As already indicated, one source of input concerns our internal state. Sense organs within the interior of the body, called **enteroceptors**, monitor aspects such as blood sugar, blood pressure, temperature and oxygen. Perception of a signal may be modulated by inputs from these sensors. For example, it is obvious how the effects of blood sugar status – being hungry or satiated – could affect your *perception* of an odour, and not hard to appreciate that it could also affect your ability to make sense of a complex image such as Figure 5.1 in Block 1.

As you may recall from Block 1, there are other sense organs throughout the body, particularly in the limbs, that monitor the position of one part of the body relative to another. These are **proprioceptors** (e.g. joint position sensors, see Figure 1.4) that provide the brain with continuous information about the position and movement of all parts of the body (the proprioceptive senses). It is obviously very important to use this information alongside the input from the external environment captured by our **exteroceptors**. These are the receptors that provide us with senses such as vision and hearing, etc. (Figure 1.4).

Figure 1.4 Examples of enteroceptors, proprioceptors and exteroceptors in the human body.

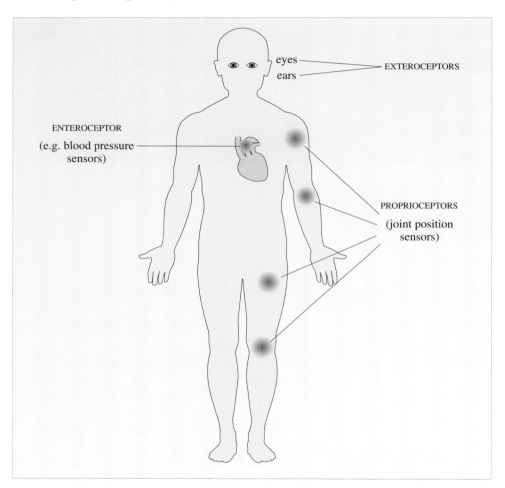

A few moments thought will reveal why integration of exteroceptive and proprioceptive information is so important. Have you ever sat on a train at a station, your only view being that of another stationary carriage? Slowly you seem to move away from the opposite carriage, only to discover that your carriage is stationary and it is the other train that is leaving the station. The image on your retina can change as a result of movement in the external world or as a result of your own movement. To respond appropriately to the external environment we must be able to distinguish between sensory input, whatever the sensory modality, that derives from events in the external environment, and sensory input that is a consequence of our own activity. We say that **exafferent** information comes from changes in the environment and **reafferent** information is due to changes in our own activities (Figure 1.5).

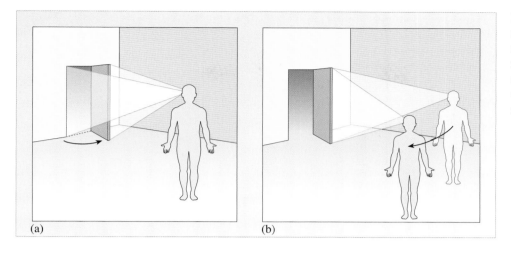

Figure 1.5 Examples of (a) exafferent input: the visual field remains constant and the person registers movement of a door; and (b) reafferent input: the field of vision changes as the person moves but the door remains still.

The **reafference principle** states that we can only respond to objects and events in our environment if our nervous system can distinguish between exafferent and reafferent information.

When you move around a room, you perceive the room as stationary because your nervous system makes allowances for the reafferent effect of both the movements of your body and movements of your eyes on the changes in sensory input to your eyes. If the door opens, the movement of the door provides a change in exafferent input; this movement can be perceived even when you are moving. Both the image of the door and the image of the walls will be moving across your retina as you move but there will be a *difference* between the rate of movement of the (stationary) wall and the (moving) door. The perceptual difficulty experienced on the stationary train arises because you were expecting to be moved and have made the appropriate adjustments. There is a different kind of perceptual problem you could experience should you ever drink too much alcohol. Then your ability to separate out exafferent information can let you down and the room you are in may appear to move. Not a pleasant experience! We will return to this later in the course when we consider the integration of the senses.

By now it will be clear to you that the old philosophical questions about the relationship between the 'real' world and our perception of it 'within our head' have rather more substance than the simplistic question: 'Is the table there if I'm not there to see it?' Although you may not see a table in an unfamiliar darkened room it is real enough and you will still walk into it. We cannot respond to a stimulus that we cannot detect. But the more interesting phenomena are the small bush that you mistake for a person as you hurriedly cross an unfamiliar park in the twilight, the moving train that turns out to be stationary and the way that you can be engrossed in one conversation, yet hear your name quite distinctly above the babble of other people's conversations if it crops up in their discussions. There is obviously much complicated processing to be done to enable us to successfully negotiate our environment. We are discovering more and more about how the system works and why it sometimes makes mistakes. It involves the activity of millions of cells, working in parallel, and we will probably never fully understand such a complex system. But we have made considerable advances recently and the story so far is fascinating and well worth studying. A good place to start is by looking at the components of the system.

Summary of Section 1

We do not passively receive information. We interact with our environment and we can exert some control over incoming signals.

Receptors acts as filters in three ways: (a) there are some stimuli that don't excite (affect) them at all; (b) some stimuli are responded to more strongly than others; (c) some kinds of processing can take place within the sense organs.

The brain processes different types of information in different regions, and the attention given to the task depends on what other activity is ongoing.

The brain appears to exert control over some incoming signals, completely suppressing them before they reach the brain.

Functional imaging techniques will help us to identify how the activity of different regions of the brain relates to perceptual constructs.

We can only respond to objects and events in our environment if our nervous system can distinguish between exafferent and reafferent information.

The human nervous system

2

The brain, the spinal cord and many peripheral nerves make up the human nervous system. The brain and spinal cord are together known as the **central nervous system** (**CNS**); the peripheral nerves are called the **peripheral nervous system** (**PNS**). They are made of delicate tissues and need special protection. The skull protects the brain, and the spinal cord is protected by the bony vertebrae of the backbone. Figure 2.1 is a diagram of the human nervous system.

In this course we are only interested in one aspect of the role of the nervous system, that is the way that it receives the **transduced** signal from the sensory receptors and how this is encoded and further processed as it travels via peripheral nerves and within the central nervous system. We will therefore study the pathways from the senses to the brain (**afferent** pathways) and the processing within the brain that leads to the perceptual construct or **percept**. Obviously, there is an output in terms

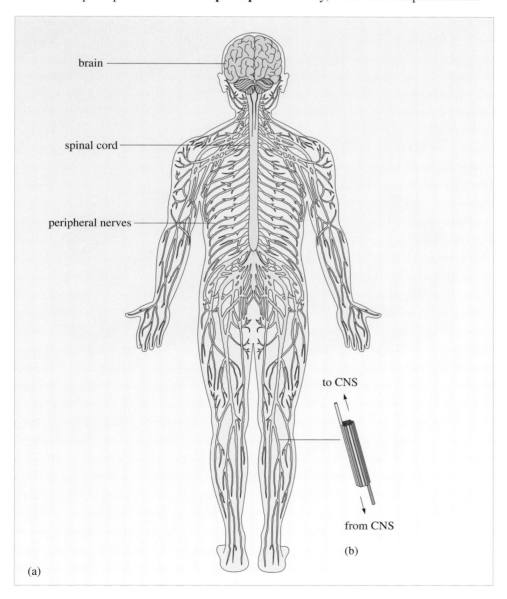

Figure 2.1 (a) The nervous system, showing the central nervous system (CNS) comprising the brain and spinal cord (pink) and the peripheral nervous system (PNS) (yellow). (b) Enlarged view of a peripheral nerve.

of behaviour and we will sometimes need to refer to that as it is the outward manifestation of the percept. However, in general we will not be discussing the **efferent** pathways, that is, those that travel from the spinal cord to the body.

The nervous system contains cells called neurons that are specialized in the rapid transport of signals throughout our bodies. Within the brain, neurons pass information within and between brain regions; they also carry out the processing that will result in our perception of the state of our internal and external world.

There are believed to be as many as 100 billion (10^{11}) neurons in the human brain. Each one can have several thousand inputs and outputs, the estimates being that there are 10–100 trillion (10^{13}–10^{14}) points of contact throughout the human nervous system. The way that neurons might be organized into functional systems can be understood at a theoretical level even if the details of the wiring cannot always be charted. Although the idea that the brain is a huge information processing organ has been around since the time of Greek philosophers and scholars such as Plato and Hippocrates, it was not possible to make much progress in studying the organ for a couple of thousand years because there were no suitable study techniques available. From time to time, it was observed that physical accidents damaged areas of brain without killing the victim of the accident and if there were subsequent altered behaviours or perceptual abilities, they could be linked to particular areas of damage known as **lesions**. Thus the idea came about that there were 'regions' of the brain, each with specific responsibilities. Dissection of brains showed anatomically distinct areas, as seen in Figure 2.2, but no further insights could be gleaned from simply describing and naming these areas.

Figure 2.2 Two views of the human brain published by the Renaissance anatomist Vesalius in 1543. In the left hand drawing the dura mater is intact, showing the smooth surface of this rugged membrane that encases the brain. In the right hand drawing, the dura mater is removed, revealing blood vessels and the pia mater, which faithfully follows the convolutions of the underlying brain tissue.

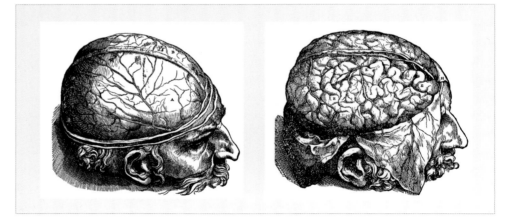

It was also obvious that there were pathways from senses, such as the eye, to the brain. On dissection, the optic nerve (Block 1, Figure 2.8) was found to have the appearance of a white, shiny thread and so, by analogy, nerves from the other parts of the body could be identified (Figure 2.1).

Even when microscopic examination became possible (Box 2.1), the cellular nature of the brain was unclear because the neurons are so branched and abut so closely onto one another that it was possible to argue that there was a continuous mesh of tissue. Figure 2.3 shows a picture of brain tissue viewed through a microscope, like those taken at the beginning of the twentieth century, and you can see for yourself how difficult it would be to decide whether there were separate cells. Nevertheless, Brodmann took slices through the **cerebral cortex**, examined them using a microscope, and used the differences he saw between them to label 47 distinct areas (Block 1, Figure 5.4).

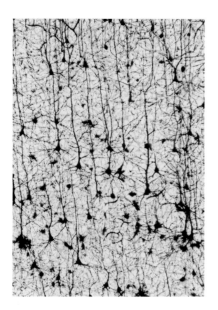

Figure 2.3   Light micrograph of pyramidal neurons from the cerebral cortex of the human brain obtained by the Golgi-Cox staining method. Branched, thread-like cell processes extend from the apex of each darkly-stained cell body towards the surface of the brain and more processes extend horizontally from the base. This technique stains single cells in their entirety. Nevertheless, it is difficult to be certain from looking at this picture that nervous tissue does consist of separate cells and not a continuous mesh of tissue.

However, by the early twentieth century, general agreement on the cellular nature of the brain was reached and, as the properties of neurons were revealed, the way was paved for a greater insight into the working of the brain and the way that messages reached it from the sensory receptors.

2.1 Cells of the nervous system

2.1.1 Structure and functions of neurons

Neurons are specialized cells for the transfer of information both *inter-* and *intra*cellularly. Uniquely, neurons act together providing a system that integrates and processes information. There are three structural features, specific to neurons, that allow them to function in this way. You will see from Figure 2.4 that there are different types of neuron but, whatever their shape, they all have a common plan.

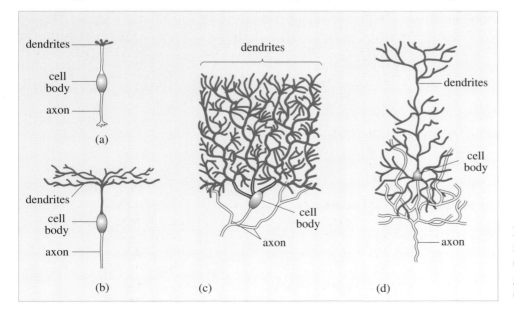

Figure 2.4   Some neurons found in the human nervous system. (a) retinal bipolar cell; (b) retinal ganglion cell; (c) cerebellar cell; (d) pyramidal cell from the cortex.

From the cell body there extends a single **axon** and a collection of **dendrites**. The dendrites and cell body receive the *inputs* to the cell; the *output* from the cell is sent down the axon.

When information is being carried by an axon we often describe it as **firing**. You will learn about the mechanisms involved later and will also discover that there is a multitude of ways of describing an active axon.

The points of contact between two neurons are known as **synapses**. Synapses are the third structural feature unique to neurons and they enable the transfer of information *between* neurons, that is, intercellular transfer.

Box 2.1   The microscopical examination and preparation of neurons

One of the great debates amongst neuroanatomists at the end of the nineteenth century concerned *dendrites*. One school of thought – founded by Gerlach in 1871, and later led by the Italian neuroanatomist, Camillo Golgi – maintained that the dendrites were continuous within the brain, so that every neuron was connected to all others by dendrites, to form a complete and continuous web of tissue. Another school – originated by Hiss in 1886, and championed by the great Spanish microscopist Santiago Ramón y Cajal – showed otherwise: that each cell and its processes (dendrites and axons) were separate. The processes touched at points but there was no continuity of tissue – one cell stopped with its border close to that of the next cell. These border points, or junctions, were called *synapses* (from the Greek meaning 'to clasp') by the British physiologist Charles Sherrington in 1897. Ramón y Cajal took the concept of the synapses and the non-continuity of brain cells and combined these ideas into what became known as the *neuronal theory*. It was, in fact, to prove correct, and the first stage in the demonstration of this was for Cajal to examine and draw cells using the light microscope.

In order to see the structure of neurons they must be made visible (Figure 2.3). Since the illuminating light of the microscope must pass through the specimen, the specimen must first be cut into slices, or sections, thin enough for light to pass through them. Prior to sectioning, the tissue is often treated with a chemical to hold the shape of the cells (a fixative) which also acts to stop the cells rotting (a preservative). The particular fixative chemical used depends on the subsequent staining procedure. Also, in order to make thin, even slices, the tissue must be hardened in some way. Tissue can be hardened by freezing, by infiltrating it with paraffin wax or by embedding it in plastic.

The tissue is sliced on an instrument somewhat resembling a miniature bacon-slicer called a microtome. The resulting sections are generally 1–40 micrometres (μm) thick.

Choosing the appropriate staining method is important. Today there are thousands of different staining methods, each designed to reveal particular features of the cells such as their nuclei or their overall shape. One of the better known neuroanatomical staining techniques was in fact developed by Camillo Golgi, in the 1880s. This Golgi technique uses various silver salts under very precise conditions. This treatment stains only a very small proportion of cells, but stains them in their entirety. The technique marked a milestone in the development of neuroscience and it was the one used by Cajal to draw his important conclusions about the basic principles of nervous system organization, the discrete nature of neurons. Golgi, however, never conceded the point, and neither scientist would speak to the other when they finally met to receive the joint award of *The Nobel Prize for Physiology or Medicine* in 1906.

Camillo Golgi (1843–1926).

Ramón y Cajal, about 1914.

Like other animal cells, the neuron's outer surface is formed by the cell membrane often known as the **plasma membrane**. This structure maintains the integrity of the neuron. It keeps the internal fluids and organelles separate from the external environment – the **extracellular** fluids. The membrane is very selective about what it will allow into the neuron and also as to what may leave. The consequence of this is that the **intracellular** fluid differs in composition from the extracellular fluid. The concentration of certain chemicals are different on the two sides of the membrane (Figure 2.5). Many of the chemicals are electrically charged, that is they are ions, so there is also a difference in charge across the membrane. One side of the membrane is relatively more positive and the other side is relatively more negative. This difference in charge is called a potential difference and the membrane is said to have a **membrane potential**. All the cells in your body have membrane potentials but the special attribute of neuronal cell membranes is the way in which they can *alter* their permeability to specific ions in a quite dramatic fashion. It is this feature that allows neurons to transfer information rapidly over long distances within the body.

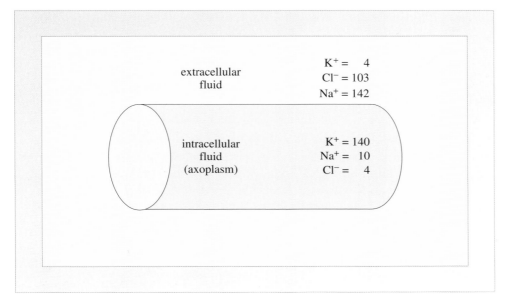

extracellular
fluid

$K^+ =$ 4
$Cl^- = 103$
$Na^+ = 142$

intracellular
fluid
(axoplasm)

$K^+ = 140$
$Na^+ =$ 10
$Cl^- =$ 4

Figure 2.5   Concentrations of some major ions on the inside and outside of an axon. Note that there are also large protein molecules with negative electrical charge found in the axoplasm. The units are millimoles/kg of fluid. Note that in addition to these ions, some others (e.g. magnesium and calcium) will also be present.

The neuron has a cell body, which contains a nucleus and other organelles. The classic picture of the neuron (see Figure 2.6 overleaf) shows the axon extending from the cell body as a very thin (less than one micrometer or micron (μm) wide) tubular extension or process, bounded by membranes and containing cytoplasm which is often referred to as **axoplasm**. The axon is usually shown as unbranched until just before its end (although many of them do branch extensively). Then it typically makes contacts with numerous other cells, each point of contact (or synapse) being described as occurring at the **axon terminal**. The axon itself may be very short, particularly in the brain where the length may be no longer than the diameter of the cell body, or may even be virtually non-existent.

On the other hand, some axons of neurons that connect between receptors in the limbs and the spinal cord will be much longer, up to a metre depending on a person's height. Although we cannot see individual axons without the aid of a microscope, it has been established that axons of many neurons in the peripheral nervous system are physically located alongside one another, and extend over the same distance, like

Figure 2.6 Simplified diagram of a typical neuron structure. The axonal terminals make synaptic contact with other neurons.

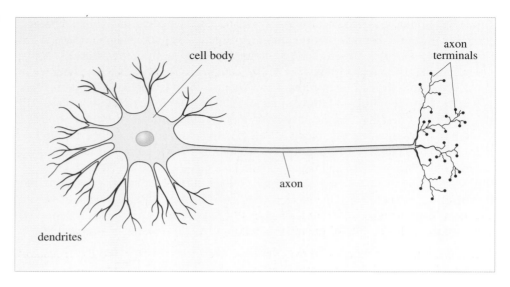

a bundle of wires in a cable of a telephone system (see Figure 2.1b). These bundles of axons can be seen and are described as **nerves**. The optic nerve (Block 1, Figure 2.8) consists of millions of neuronal axons of retinal ganglion cells (see Figure 2.4b) and constitutes the pathway that conveys information from the eyes to the brain. To avoid confusion, we only use the term 'nerve' to refer to these bundles of axons and always use 'neuron' when referring to a single cell.

To continue with our description of the unique features of neurons, we turn to the structure of dendrites. Dendrites are also tubular, membrane-bound extensions from the cell body that are filled with cytoplasm. They tend to be shorter, much thicker and more highly branched than the axon, and their networks of branches are often called dendritic trees. There may be many dendritic processes extending from the cell body in contrast to the single axon. Figure 2.7 shows a three-dimensional computer reconstruction of part of a dendrite.

Dendritic spines are the protrusions on the surface of the dendrite. They are the synaptic input sites.

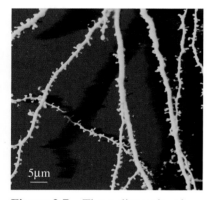

Figure 2.7 Three-dimensional computer reconstruction of part of a dendrite showing the dendritic spines.

○ What value might there be in having these protuberances as the points of contact between neurons?

● You may have thought that because these protuberances provide a greater surface area for synapses this would increase the number of inputs that could be made, but this doesn't seem to be the case. The advantage of this arrangement of spines lies in their being elevated away from the dendrite. From this position these spines are easier to enlarge or shrink as the efficacy of the synapse is increased or reduced in, for example, memory circuits.

The shapes of dendrites and axons are maintained by an internal **cytoskeleton**. This is a well ordered system of tube-like structures called microtubules, much smaller microfilaments and intermediate-sized neurofilaments as shown in Figure 2.8.

Table 2.1 indicates that the elements of the cytoskeleton are not just responsible for the development and maintenance of the axonal and dendrite structure. They also provide a transport system to move proteins synthesized in the cell body to the axon terminals. Some of these proteins will be required for routine metabolic activity.

Table 2.1   Functions of the major elements of the neuronal cytoskeleton.

Name	Function
microtubules	axonal protein transport, development and maintenance of structure
neurofilaments	not known (get 'tangled' in disease)
microfilaments	thought to assist in control of movement in developing neurons

Others are molecules, called **neurotransmitters**, which have specific shapes and chemical functions so that they can be released from the end of the axon and cross the tiny (20–50 nanometres (nm) wide) synaptic gap to the neighbouring neuron. Here they influence the activity of the neuron making it either more or less likely to fire.

When information is transferred from the axon terminal of one cell to a part (usually the dendrite or cell body) of another cell by the release of a neurotransmitter, the synapse is described as a **chemical synapse** (Figure 2.9a). The other kind of synapse is an **electrical synapse** (see Figure 2.9b). Here information is passed between cells as an electrical signal. This occurs rapidly whereas the chemical synapse creates a delay in the pathway of about 1 millisecond (ms) or longer. Whilst the basic concepts of synaptic mechanism are fairly straightforward, the variation in detail is immense. There will be more discussion of this in Section 3.3.2.

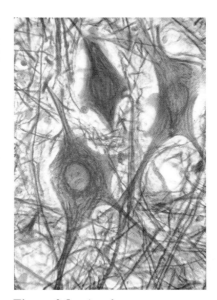

Figure 2.8   An electron micrograph of neurons that demonstrate 2–3 μm thick elongated strands in their cytoplasm and processes. These structures are the neurofibrils and constitute the neuron's cytoskeleton. They provide structural support for the cell body, dendrites and especially for axons that sometimes extend as far as one metre away from the cell body.

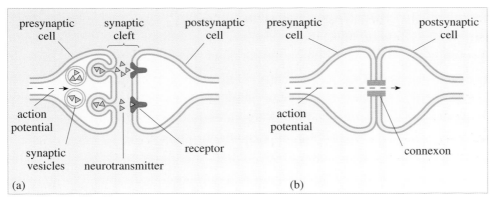

(a)   (b)

Figure 2.9   Chemical and electrical synaptic transmission. (a) At a chemical synapse, the arrival of an electrical impulse (action potenital) at the presynaptic neuron terminal triggers the release of neurotransmitter molecules, which interact with receptors on the postsynaptic neuron, causing excitation or inhibition. (b) At electrical synapses, current flows directly from one cell to another through connexons or intercellular channels that cluster to form gap junctions.

The transfer of information intracellularly towards the axon terminal does not involve proteins flowing along the axonal structures of the cytoskeleton, that would be far too slow! It would take a full day for a protein to diffuse along a 1 millimetre (mm) section of axon and even the fastest methods of axonal protein transport can only achieve rates of around a few hundred millimetres per day. By contrast, information can flash along axons at speeds of up to 100 metres per second (m s^{-1}). This information is carried as electrical signals (Box 2.2, p. 84) and the neuron is described as 'firing' when it carries these signals. The structure of the axonal membrane is specialized to allow this to happen.

We will need to study the structure of neuronal membranes in some detail later (Section 3.2) because it gives us tremendous insight into the mechanisms that allow the nervous system to respond flexibly. For the moment we will note that the effect of a neurotransmitter arriving at the postsynaptic cell is to change the electrical state of the postsynaptic cell membrane at that point (usually on a dendritic spine; Figure 2.7). This change may be excitatory or inhibitory and is called a **synaptic potential**. If the cumulative effect of transmitters arriving at the dendrites and cell body of one neuron produces a change in the electrical state of the axonal membrane at the **axon hillock** (which is the transition area between the axon and the cell body; see Figure 2.10) that exceeds a **threshold** level, then a wave of electrical activity is discharged along the axon. This is called an **action potential** and it travels along the axon from the point of initiation to the synaptic terminals. Action potentials are the basic language of the nervous system. The function of a neuron is to sum the effects of the inputs arriving at its dendrites and cell body (of which there may be thousands) and when appropriate to generate action potentials. These are sent toward the next element(s) in its pathway, which may be another neuron (or neurons) or a muscle or a secretory cell (see Figure 2.10).

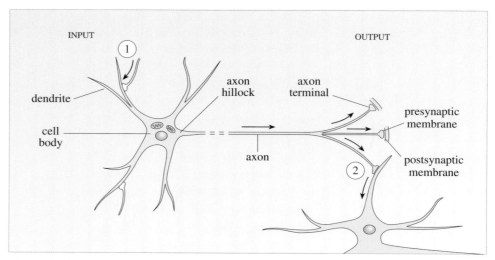

Figure 2.10   Sketch of a neuron synapsing with other neurons. Synapses (e.g. synapse 1) bring signals to this neuron. Other synapses (e.g. synapse 2) influence other cells. The action potential arises at the part of the axon which is closest to the cell body, known as the axon hillock.

Local changes in cell membrane potential, or voltage (the volt is the unit of electrical potential), that result from neurotransmitter acting upon the postsynaptic membrane (synaptic potentials) depend on the strength of incoming activity and the size of the synapse. They are therefore *graded* and related to the number and type of membrane-bound **receptor** * sites that are activated by the neurotransmitter molecules. This is an extremely important feature of nerve signalling because it

---

* It should be clear from the context when we are talking about receptors in cell membranes as opposed to sensory receptors which are whole cells.

allows different stimuli to generate different responses. The change in membrane potential spreads from the point of origin and, although it diminishes with distance, if it reaches a critical or threshold level at the axon hillock, an action potential of a fixed magnitude is generated. The neuron is said to 'fire' and the critical membrane potential threshold required for this to happen is often described as the 'firing threshold'. The action potential's amplitude does not change appreciably as it travels along the length of the axon. In contrast to the graded response of the postsynaptic membrane to transmitter substances, the action potential either occurs in full or not at all. The action potential is, therefore, often described as an **all-or-nothing response**. The upper limit to the rate at which axons can transmit electrical impulses along their length is around 1000 action potentials per second (1000 Hz). For any one axon, the speed of conduction of action potentials along the length of an axon is relatively constant but different axons conduct at different speeds (Table 2.2). Table 2.2 shows that there is a similar situation relating to the duration of the action potential. By contrast, the synaptic potential can last much longer, typically up to 8 ms.

Table 2.2 Classification of mammalian nerve fibres.*

Fibre types	Fibre diameter/μm	Conduction velocity/m s^{-1}	Duration of spike/ms	Function
Aα	13–22	70–120	0.4–0.5	motor, muscle proprioception
Aβ	8–13	40–70	0.4–0.6	touch, pressure, kinesthesis
Aγ	4–8	15–40	0.5–0.7	touch, innervation of muscle spindles
Aδ	1–4	5–15	0.6–1.0	pain, heat, cold and pressure
B	1–3	3–14	1.2	autonomic[†]
C	0.2–1	0.2–2.0	2.0	pain, itch, heat, cold, pressure, smell, autonomic

* Fibres can be used as a collective term to cover axons and dendrites but is also sometimes used instead of either axons or dendrites.

† The nervous system concerned with regulating the activity of internal organs, e.g. heart, gut, glands.

It is the *rate* of firing (i.e. the frequency or number of action potentials generated per second) or the *change of frequency* of action potentials that is the language of these neurons. But it was mentioned earlier that many of the neurons in the brain have axons that are *very* short, i.e. no longer than their cell bodies. These neurons will *respond* to their various synaptic inputs as do neurons with long axons. They process the incoming information and, if appropriate, they will pass information to other neurons. However, very short axons (less than 1 mm in length) do not generate action potentials, rather their membrane potential changes in a graded fashion. The reason for the relationship between length of axon and generation of action potentials can be put simplistically: we can say that the graded response mechanism would not work for long distances. This will become clear when we look at the molecular events that underlie the functioning of neurons in Section 3.

Box 2.2   The history of recording nerve activity

The electrical nature of neural activity was first demonstrated in the middle of the eighteenth century by Luigi Galvani. He observed that the frogs' legs he was dissecting on a zinc plate jumped when he touched the nerve with a metal object. (Incidentally, this observation also led to the invention of the battery.)

The electrical signals produced by neurons are very small (measured in millivolts (mV); 1 mV is a thousandth of a volt) and brief (measured in milliseconds (ms); 1 ms is one thousandth of a second). Monitoring the activity of neurons therefore requires sophisticated techniques of amplification and display that were first developed in the 1930s and have been refined and upgraded more or less continually since then.

Traditionally, the simplest way to monitor or record action potentials was to lay a nerve (or in some special cases, part of an individual neuron) across two wires (called electrodes) and to measure the potential between the electrodes during the conduction of an

action potential produced either by natural stimulation (e.g. of sensory receptors) or by electrical stimulation. The potential was first amplified and then used to move a pen that drew an ink trace on a moving paper chart. The greater the signal, the greater the deflection of the pen. As the paper moved past the pen it therefore drew a graph of the change in potential with time. Action potentials displayed in this way have a characteristic spiky shape, and are sometimes referred to as nerve spikes. Figure 2.11a shows the typical experimental set-up and Figure 2.11b shows what recordings of membrane potentials look like.

Initially, work was carried out on very large axons taken from the squid. These squid giant axons are up to 1 mm (millimetre) in diameter, 100 times the diameter of even the largest axon found in humans. They could be extracted from the squid and kept alive as a *tissue preparation* (biological material that has been prepared in some way so that it can be studied) in a glass

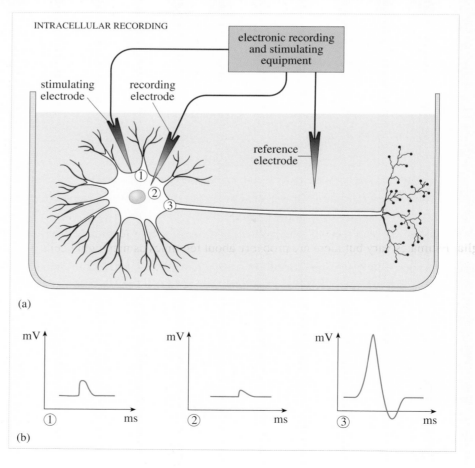

Figure 2.11   (a) Brief electrical impulses are delivered through the stimulating electrode. The recording electrode can then be positioned at various points on the neuron. (b) Hypothetical results from an experiment where a single pulse delivered through the stimulating electrode was picked up by a recording device (voltmeter) connected to recording electrodes at points 1, 2 and 3. Note that the signal has attenuated between positions 1 and 2, nevertheless there has been sufficient potential reaching 3 (the axon hillock) to generate an action potential.

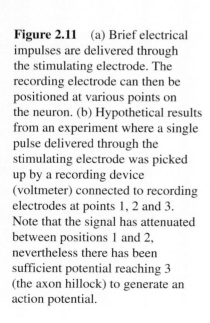

container (often known as an organ bath) containing fluid of composition identical to that of the extracellular fluid of the squid (Figure 2.11a).

Nowadays, neurophysiologists do not use paper, but instead use a device called an oscilloscope to display nerve activity. In an oscilloscope the potential is displayed as the vertical deflection of an electronic beam which hits a phosphor screen rather like a television or electron microscope screen. The electron beam moves across the screen at a constant rate, which can be altered just like the paper speed in the chart recorder. Much higher speeds are possible using this method. Advances in microelectronics make it possible to measure the potentials and store and analyse the traces using computers. You may have seen similar computer-based equipment used in hospitals to monitor brain or heart activity.

Similarly, over the years, greatly refined experimental procedures for electrical recordings have been developed. Very fine electrodes made from fluid-filled glass tubing with a small fluid-filled bore (micropipettes) are now available. These then serve as microelectrodes, as shown schematically in Figure 2.11.

In this way it is possible to produce microelectrodes with tips so fine (about 0.1 μm) that they can penetrate the membranes of all but the smallest neurons without disturbing their function. Glass microelectrodes with larger tips (greater than 1 μm) are less prone to breakage, but these can only be used for extracellular recording. In this case, the electrode is moved close to the cell membrane to pick up its electrical activity. It is possible to record action potentials through both extracellular and intracellular microelectrodes. The resting membrane potential and small fluctuations in membrane potential such as synaptic potentials can be recorded only with intracellular electrodes.

The microelectrode is filled with a concentrated ionic solution so that, at the exposed tip, it is in electrical contact with the recording site, but is electrically insulated elsewhere. A silver wire is normally inserted into the wide end of the electrode and this serves as a link between the fluid inside the microelectrode and the connections to the recording apparatus. A connection is also made to the fluid bathing the outside of the axon (the reference electrode), so that the difference in potential across the membrane is recorded (Figure 2.11b).

One might imagine that the impaling of an axon or cell body in this way, penetrating its membrane, would seriously disrupt those processes that one wishes to observe, but the evidence is that the disruption can be minimal. To stimulate the neuron, an external source of electrical current can be connected to the microelectrode to change the potential difference between the inside and outside of the cell. This is delivered via the stimulating electrode and it simulates what happens when a neuron fires in response to an external stimulus such as a touch or a smell.

2.1.2 Non-neural cells in the nervous system – the glial cells and others

Neurons are not the only cells in the nervous system, indeed they are in the minority. Far more numerous is a heterogeneous category of cells known collectively as the **glia**. Estimates vary but there are probably about ten times as many glial cells as neurons in the human nervous system and they are mostly much smaller.

For a long time the glial cells were thought to be little more than 'glue', holding the nervous system together. It is still thought that one of their roles is to provide structure in much the same way as connective tissue does in other organs but there is now evidence for several other functions. Of these, the best known and best understood is the provision of insulating material around neuronal axons. **Myelin** is the name of the thick, whitish, electrically insulating fatty material. It is formed during development by the glial cells. Areas of the CNS where there is a lot of myelin are referred to as **white matter**, contrasting with **grey matter** areas where there are densely packed cell bodies. Myelin is not found around all axons in the nervous system but it is crucial to the functioning of those which are myelinated. This is demonstrated tragically by the symptoms experienced by people who suffer from demyelinating diseases, such as multiple sclerosis. In Section 3 you will learn more about the biology of this disease.

It has already been stated that different axons conduct at different speeds and the presence of myelin is a factor that affects speed of conduction. Myelinated axons conduct action potentials more speedily than unmyelinated axons.

○ Use Table 2.2 to describe another structural property that affects speed of conduction.

● The diameter of the fibre affects speed of conduction.

○ What type of fibre would allow the most rapid conduction of action potentials?

● According to the table, fibre type Aα allows the most rapid conduction speed. This is the fibre with the largest cross-sectional diameter and it is clear from the table that conduction speed is directly related to axon diameter.

The mechanisms involved in this relationship will be discussed in Section 3.

The myelin sheath is formed by the glial cell wrapping itself around the axon many times. As its hold on the axon tightens, all the cytoplasm is squeezed out of that part of the glial cell, leaving layers of glial cell membrane around the axon. In cross-section the appearance is a little like a Swiss roll – as can be seen in Figure 2.12. Figure 2.12a and 2.12b show diagrammatic cross-sections of glial cells from different parts of the nervous system. Figure 2.12a illustrates cells taken from the brain where a type of glial cell called an **oligodendrocyte** is responsible for all the myelin sheathing in the central nervous system. **Schwann cells** (Figure 2.12b and c) form myelin sheaths around neurons in the peripheral nervous system.

○ What differences do you notice between the arrangement of myelin in relation to the axons in Figure 2.12a and 2.12b?

● The oligodendrocyte is wrapped around several different axons (three are shown here but it can be more). The Schwann cell is around one axon only.

You should also notice areas labelled **node of Ranvier**. Here there are breaks in the myelin sheath. Each Schwann cell only wraps around a small portion of the axon, the nodes of Ranvier being the gaps between these glial cells and the gaps occurring every 1–2 mm along the axon. Nodes of Ranvier are also found on axons of neurons of the central nervous system. They are formed by an oligodendrocyte wrapping around different sections of the same axon. As we shall see in Section 3, this arrangement is of great significance in facilitating the speedy passage of electrical signals along the axon. The precise chemical make-up of the Schwann cell myelin differs from that of oligodendrocytes and it may account for the ability of peripheral axons to recover from certain types of damage.

Many peripheral axons are very long (for example, those that when bundled together, make up the sciatic nerve in your leg) and there will be many individual Schwann cells contributing to the myelin sheath around each axon. We will discover why all but the very shortest axons need to have breaks in the myelin sheath in Section 3.

Oligodendrocytes are one of the most numerous cell types in the CNS and they are known to have two other functions. They form rows of semi-rigid tissue between neurons which is believed to provide structural support and they also supply nutrients to neurons. This latter function benefits unmyelinated neurons as well as the myelinated ones. As there are many more glial cells than neurons, no CNS

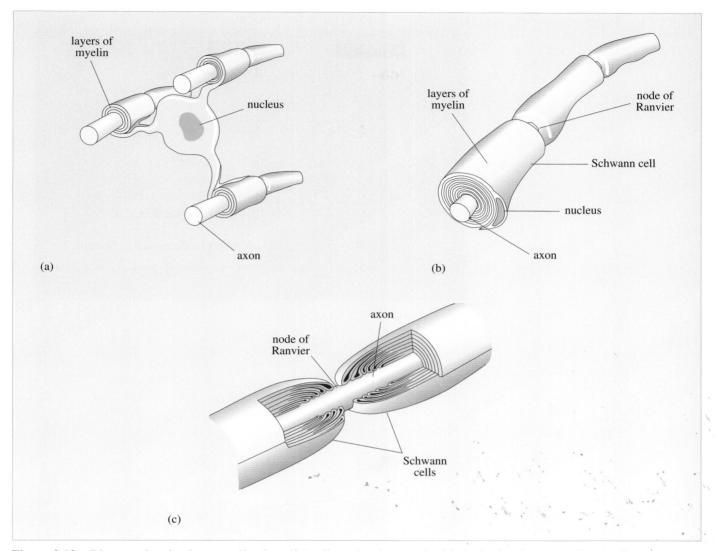

layers of
myelin

nucleus

axon

(a)

layers of
myelin

node of
Ranvier

Schwann cell

nucleus

axon

(b)

axon

node of
Ranvier

Schwann
cells

(c)

Figure 2.12   Diagram showing how myelinating glial cells ensheath axons in: (a) the brain where one oligodendrocyte wraps around several axons; and (b) a peripheral nerve where a Schwann cell wraps around one axon. (c) A Schwann cell cut away to show the arrangement of membrane layers adjacent to a node of Ranvier.

neuron is far away from an oligodendrocyte and so all neurons are surrounded by glial cells, even if not wrapped in myelin. In the peripheral nervous system (PNS) it is **satellite cells** (also called capsule cells) that help to protect, nourish and maintain neurons.

The other type of glia found in large numbers in the CNS is the **astrocyte**. These star-shaped cells can be seen in Figure 2.13 (overleaf). They fill the spaces between neurons and twine around them giving structural support. They can also be seen in Figure 2.14 (overleaf) with the terminals of their cytoplasmic processes embracing a blood vessel in the CNS.

It was thought that this structural arrangement of astrocytes formed the **blood–brain barrier**, so called because there are many chemicals that are unable to pass from the blood supply into the extracellular fluid of the brain, although they pass freely into

Figure 2.13 Immunofluorescence micrograph showing astrocyte cells in the brain. (Immunofluorescence is a staining technique which uses antibodies to attach fluorescent dyes to specific tissues and molecules.)

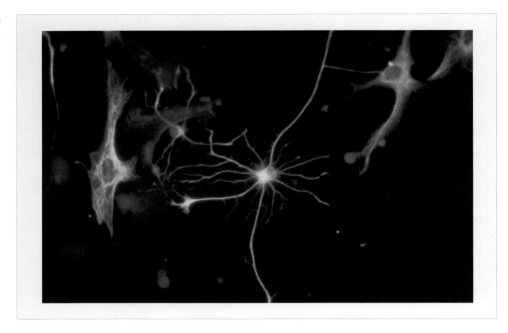

Figure 2.14 A schematic illustration of the arrangement of astrocytes at the blood-brain barrier.

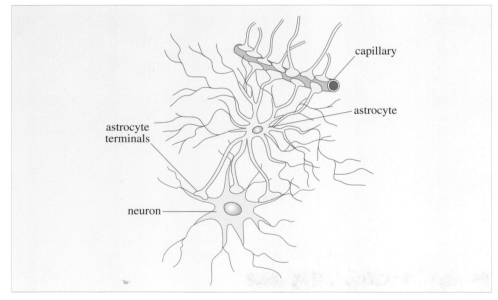

other organs. Recent evidence for this role being taken by astrocytes is less convincing. It was thought that the astrocytes terminal processes created the fatty barrier through which non-fat soluble substances are unable to pass, but it now seems that the epithelial cells of the blood capillaries adjoin one another so closely that they prevent the substances from slipping through spaces between cells (Figure 2.14). The role of the astrocyte terminals (also called end feet) is now thought to relate to the supply of oxygen and glucose being delivered to neurons. Specifically, the suggestion is that astrocytes register the local metabolic requirements and, via their end feet, signal for the blood capillaries to dilate. This increase in size translates to an increased flow of blood into the local area thereby allowing the higher demand for oxygen and nutrients to be met. This is a feature that is utilized in one method of brain imaging that you will meet in Section 4.

Astrocytes also have a role in 'mopping up' leaked or released neurotransmitter and in regulating the extracellular fluid composition, particularly the potassium (K^+) ion concentration. Potassium ion fluctuations are particularly significant in the generation of action potentials as you will read in Section 3.

Although we have examined the unique structures that specialize neurons for inter- and intracellular signalling, and it has long been thought that only neurons can perform those functions, we are beginning to revise some of these ideas as more is revealed of glial activity. In particular, the astrocytes may have a role in brain signalling. Some of the evidence is circumstantial; receptors are found on the surface of astrocytes that are capable of responding to certain neurotransmitters. Research has shown that if cultured astrocytes are artificially stimulated by these neurotransmitters, oscillations can be set up in their cytoplasmic calcium (Ca^{2+}) ion concentrations which can spread to both neighbouring astrocytes and neurons. As we shall see in Section 3, Ca^{2+} ions play an important part in the process of passing information across chemical synapses, so this is strongly suggestive of a signalling capability both between astrocytes and between astrocytes and neurons.

Microglia are smaller glial cells only found in the CNS, see Figure 2.15. They act as brain scavengers, engulfing and destroying bacteria and debris from dead and dying neurons and glia.

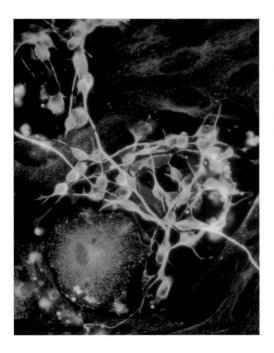

Figure 2.15 Immunofluorescence micrograph of a macrophage within brain tissue. Macrophages found in nervous tissue are termed microglia. This large scavenger cell (stained red, lower left) moves in search of bacteria and other foreign material to ingest. At centre, a tangle of neurons with interconnected nerve fibres stains green.

The **ependymal** cells that form a layer lining the brain **ventricles** and the **central canal** of the spinal cord are also glial cells. At the end of this section you are asked to undertake Activity 2.1 and you will see an artist's impression of astrocytes, microglia and ependymal cells on the DVD material.

○ Are the ependymal cells found in the peripheral nervous system?

● No, brain and spinal cord are the central nervous system.

The ventricles and central canal contain a fluid known as **cerebrospinal fluid (CSF)**, which is also found in the *subarachnoid* space around the brain and spinal cord (Figure 2.16). The fluid circulates in a definite pathway around all these interconnected spaces. The ependymal cells are one of the sources of the fluid; they secrete it and may assist in its circulation. The fluid helps to cushion the brain and spinal cord if they suffer trauma.

In conclusion, it is clear that glial cells have important structural, protective and insulating functions within the nervous system, but it seems increasingly likely that their role may extend beyond this, perhaps even to information transfer. Although not particularly relevant to this course, it should be noted in passing that they are involved in the development of the nervous system. Thus they might also hold one of the keys to a better understanding of neuronal repair. This makes them of great interest to many researchers and you should not be surprised if you find glial cells moving into the research spotlight in years to come.

Figure 2.16   A diagram of brain structure showing fluid-filled spaces and protective sheets of tissue.

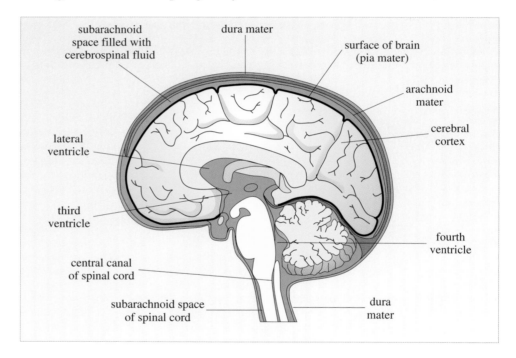

Summary of Section 2.1

Neurons and glial cells are the constituents of the nervous system, which can be conveniently divided into the two anatomically and functionally discrete systems of the central nervous system (CNS) and the peripheral nervous system (PNS).

Neurons are information processing devices and have specialized processes, axons and dendrites, for this purpose. They are functionally connected to one another by synapses. Signalling across synapses may be electrical or chemical but the receiving neuron will ultimately respond with a changed membrane potential called a synaptic potential. Whether information gets passed to the next element in the chain depends upon whether the total synaptic input to the neuron has led to a sufficient change in membrane potential in a specialized area (the axon hillock) to reach a threshold potential value that initiates the generation of an action potential. The action potential is an all-or-nothing response; the membrane potential changes associated with it fluctuate in a constant way that can be visually displayed as a 'spike' on an oscilloscope. This contrasts with the graded response recorded at the postsynaptic membrane of the receiving neuron. The level of this response depends on the strength of the incoming stimulation and may be excitatory or inhibitory.

The speed of conduction of action potentials is constant along the length of an axon and depends on the diameter of the axon and whether or not it is myelinated. Large diameter axons conduct faster than small diameter axons; myelinated axons conduct faster than unmyelinated ones.

Myelin is the insulation provided by glial cells – Schwann cells in the PNS, oligodendrocytes in the CNS. Glial cells also provide support and structure to the nervous system. They have 'housekeeping' duties, nourishing nervous tissue by regulating the supply of nutrients and protecting by mopping up debris and buffering ions in the extracellular fluid.

The important message from this section, upon which you will be building later in this and other blocks, is that whilst postsynaptic potentials are graded, action potentials are all-or-nothing response. Action potentials are conducted along an axon at constant speed, but the rate of discharge can vary, and that it is this rate of discharge or the change in rate of discharge that is the language of the nervous system.

Activity 2.1

This is a good time to take a break from reading and use *The Senses* multimedia program on the DVD. This covers much of the material you've read about, and will help to consolidate your learning and prepare you for the next section. Further instructions are given in the Block 2 *Study File*.

Question 2.1

What particular property of the cell membrane is so important to neural function?

Question 2.2

What is the principal difference between an action potential and a synaptic potential?

Question 2.3

Outline the sequence of events following the arrival of an action potential at the chemical synapse of an axon terminal.

2.2 Sensation to perception

2.2.1 The sense of touch

Having reviewed the components of the nervous system and studied some anatomy, we will now show how neurons work together to enable us to be aware of our surroundings. We will be concentrating in particular on the sense of touch, which is one of the somatosensory or contact senses.

○ From your study of *The Senses* DVD you should be able to name the other somatosensory senses and to say whether they are categorized as *general* or *special* senses.

● Temperature, pressure, pain and touch are the somatosensory senses and they are categorized as general senses because the sensory receptors involved have a widespread distribution whilst the special senses have receptors in restricted areas only (e.g. light receptors are located in the eye, auditory receptors in the ear).

For both touch and pressure, the stimulus to which the sensory receptors respond is a mechanical one. They are, therefore, **mechanoreceptors**.

○ Where are the receptors for touch and pressure to be found?

● Receptors for both are **cutaneous** but pressure receptors are also located in deep tissues throughout the body.

The sense of touch is also sometimes described as *light touch* to distinguish it clearly from pressure. The touch receptor responds when a mechanical stimulus causes deformation of the skin. Pressure is equivalent to sustained touch; receptors respond when the deformation of the skin is greater and the stimulus lasts longer. The response to pressure lasts longer than that to light touch, it shows less variation in intensity and is felt over a larger area. A third, and related, sense is vibration which is a continuing periodic change in displacement of a stimulus with respect to a fixed point.

Touch is the sense that provides information about stimuli in the external environment that make actual physical contact or come very close to the surface of our bodies. The objects that are out there in the world are described as **distal** (far) objects and the pattern of information, carried by the pressure variation which reaches the sensory receptor, is called the **proximal** (near) stimulus. Distal and proximal are terms that are used for all sensory modalities. The distal object and the proximal stimulus may be nothing like each other, and our task is to understand how, given only proximal stimuli, the brain reconstructs the world of distal objects in which we live. The relationship between the proximal stimulus and the distal object is complex but there is a school of thought that maintains that proximal stimuli contain all the information needed for perception. This approach, pioneered by the American psychologist James Gibson, is called *direct perception* and it views perception as essentially a process of picking up information from the environment. An alternative view proposes that, because proximal and distal phenomena are so different from one another, simple picking up of information really is not enough. Even if they can derive a complete description of the proximal stimulus, perceptual systems still face the subtle and difficult task of working out what produced it. So perception is an active process, endlessly trying to make sense of the fleeting glimpses of reality provided by the sense organs. In this section we take just one sense, touch, and follow the path from signal to perception, considering whether, in the final analysis, we subscribe to the direct or the indirect school.

We established in Block 1 that signals from the distal object do not act directly on the brain. The brain receives information about stimuli by means of coded electrical signals that propagate (travel) along afferent neurons. The first stage in this process is the conversion or transduction of the stimulus energy (pressure in this case) into the language of the nervous system – action potentials. This transduction is the role of the sensory receptor. Figure 2.17 illustrates the general neural pathway from sensory receptor to brain initiated by a touch stimulus. But to touch is to perceive more than absence or presence of pressure; we can feel the difference between silk and velvet, water and oil, or wood and metal. Somehow action potentials must encode information about various properties of the stimulus.

○   What features of the stimulus might be coded in the signals transmitted to the brain?

●   The nerve impulse discharge could code information about:

(i)   what the stimulus is (*quality*);

(ii)   how large the stimulus is (*intensity*);

(iii)   the timing of the stimulus (*duration*);

(iv)   where it is (*location*).

We will consider how information about these features may be coded and communicated along different pathways to the brain.

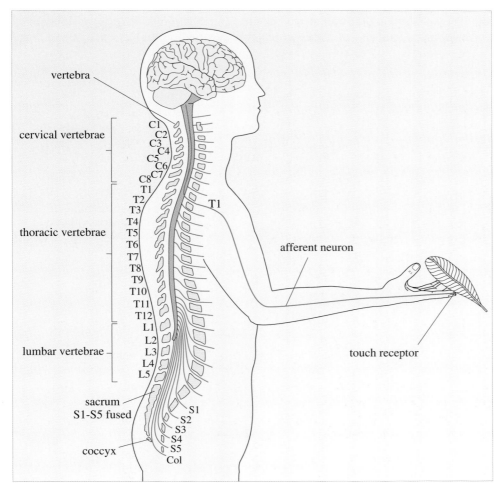

Figure 2.17   A schematic representation of one neural pathway from a touch receptor in the finger to the brain.

2.2.2 Sensory coding by mechanoreceptors

Figure 2.17 does not give us the sufficiently fine anatomical details that we need to continue our investigation of sensory coding. Figure 2.18 shows the structure of the skin and the **morphology** (form or structure) of some of the receptors.

The question of stimulus *quality* is determined by the type of sensory receptor that is activated by the stimulus. Receptors respond selectively to specific stimuli, and there are many different kinds of receptor, each tuned to detect their own particular stimulus modality (also called the *adequate stimulus*). Figure 2.18 shows the skin to have a variety of receptors, each of which has its own adequate stimulus. These receptors have characteristic structures, and many are named after the person who first identified them. There will be more about them in Block 5, but you might immediately notice a feature that could compromise their ability to signal quality.

○   What are the adequate stimuli for **Meissner's corpuscles**?

●   Meissner's corpuscles respond to both light touch and to vibration.

○   How does this compromise their ability to signal quality?

●   This means that they do not send an unambiguous signal. Clearly, at some point, there must be a way of deducing whether the stimulus was a light touch or vibration.

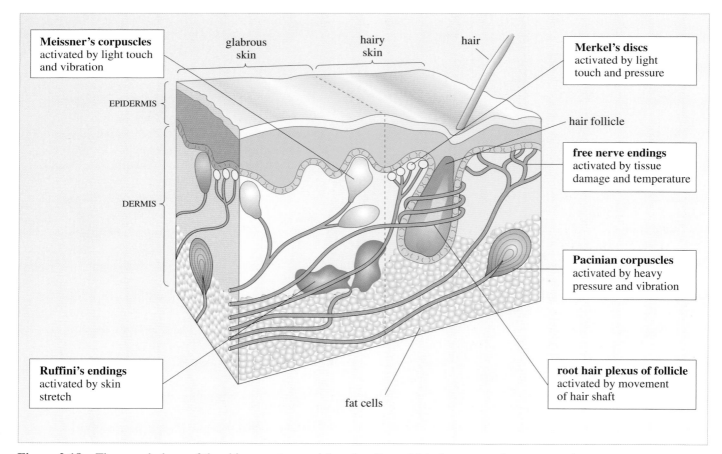

Figure 2.18   The morphology of the skin receptors and the stimuli to which they respond.

○ Can you see (from Figure 2.18) how this might be achieved?

● **Merkel's discs** respond to light touch and pressure, **Pacinian corpuscles** respond to heavy pressure and vibration, so if Merkel's discs and Meissner's corpuscles are active but Pacinian corpuscles are showing no response, the stimulus must be light touch.

When we come to look more closely at the anatomy of the sensory pathways we will see that there is no possibility of this computation taking place in the skin, it must occur within the CNS.

Although the morphology of these skin mechanoreceptors is diverse, they all, in common with all other sensory receptors, respond to their adequate stimulus by altering their electrical activity. This is the transduction process and this altered potential is called the **receptor potential** (sometimes called the generator potential). The change in receptor potential is a *graded response*. The receptor potential increases in size with the size (*intensity*) of the stimulus. Many receptor cells, such as those in your eyes, can only generate a receptor potential and cannot generate action potentials but the skin mechanoreceptors are modified sensory neurons and have axons that can carry an action potential. The action potential is an all-or-nothing response with a threshold below which no action potential is generated. Only when the receptor potential exceeds a certain value will action potentials be generated along the axon of the skin mechanoreceptor.

○ How can the graded response of the receptor potential be used to signal the size (*intensity*) of the stimulus?

● Whilst a larger stimulus produces a bigger receptor potential this can only convert to a fixed size action potential, so the only possibility is to alter the interval *between* each action potential.

Thus a larger stimulus will produce a more rapid burst of firing of action potentials. The intensity of the stimulus determines action potential frequency (rate); this is called *frequency coding*.

The relationship between stimulus intensity, amplitude of receptor potential and frequency of action potentials is summarized in Figure 2.19 (overleaf). Figure 2.19a shows the arrangement for an experiment in which the receptor potential and action potential responses of one sensory neuron are monitored while pressure is applied to its **receptive field** on the skin of the finger. Its receptive field is the area of skin any part of which will, when touched, cause that particular cell to respond. Figure 2.19b shows the relationship between the intensity of stimulation, the receptor potential and the neuron's action potentials. As the intensity of stimulation is increased (S_1–S_3), you can see that the amplitude of the receptor potentials increases and there is an increase in frequency of action potentials in R_2 and R_3. The 'results' of this hypothetical experiment (i.e. the relationship between stimulus intensity and response of the neuron) are shown in Figure 2.19c. Here a graph has been drawn that represents the frequency of action potentials or 'firing rate' of the afferent neuron to a wide range of different stimulus intensities. The point T is called the *threshold* for the neuron. (Note that no receptor displays a perfectly regular discharge because firing rates are not perfectly regular. To draw this graph required the experimenter to repeat the experiment many times and the values plotted are averaged.)

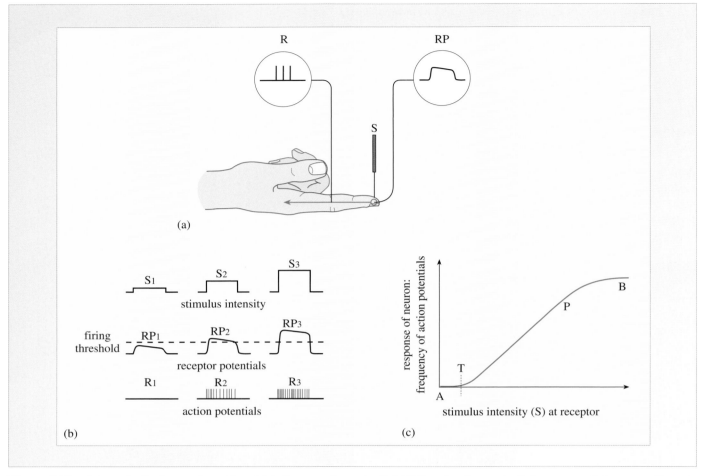

Figure 2.19   A hypothetical experiment in which the receptor potential (RP) and action potential response R from an afferent neuron are monitored during application of pressure stimuli (S) to the skin. Although the application of S will cause more than one receptor to respond, we are only recording from the axon of one neuron. See text for details of the experiment.

○ Look at the relationship between stimulus intensity and response of the sensory neuron. What happens between points A and T?

● No action potentials are generated by stimuli of these intensities. This is because the receptor potential is below the firing threshold for action potential firing, as is the case for stimulus S_1 in Figure 2.19b.

○ What happens between points T and P?

● With a stimulus value greater than T, action potentials are generated. Between points T and P the graph is approximately a straight line. This indicates that the neuron firing rate (frequency) between these points is roughly proportional to the intensity of the stimulus.

○ What happens between points P and B?

● Further increases in stimulus intensity produce little increase in frequency of response.

Point P marks the start of a plateau on the graph, indicating that the linear relationship between stimulus and response has broken down. The response of the neuron is *saturated*, which means that further increases in stimulus intensity do not result in an increase in response, which remains at approximately the same level.

Individual sensory receptors do not respond over the whole range of stimulus intensities. Some have low thresholds, while others are activated only by relatively intense stimuli. At the macrolevel we have already divided the mechanoreceptors found in the skin into those that respond to light touch and those that respond to pressure.

Another mechanism, which contributes to the process of coding stimulus intensity, is the number of receptors and afferent neurons activated. Each afferent neuron and its terminal branches is grouped in a well-defined area which constitutes the receptive field of that sensory neuron, or mechanoreceptor. Some areas of skin are more richly supplied with mechanoreceptors than others.

○   How will this affect the coding of stimulus intensity?

●   A weak stimulus will recruit a response from more receptors when applied to some areas of skin than when applied to other parts of the body's surface. Stronger stimuli will cause a greater amount of skin indentation. This increased stimulation will activate receptors which have higher thresholds for activation as well as those that are sensitive to light touch but lie further away from the point of stimulation.

This means that somewhere in the CNS the meaning to be attached to the number and type of receptors responding has to be assessed against the information as to the origin of the transduced signal.

We cannot understand how *location* is coded until we have examined the complete somatosensory pathway from receptor to brain. Meantime, we now know that the coding of stimulus intensity involves variations in (i) the frequency of action potential in the afferent neurons, and (ii) the number of neurons that are activated.

○   How could the *duration* of a stimulus be coded?

●   The simplest way would be for the action potential discharge to continue as long as the stimulus is applied, for example, as shown in Figure 2.19b.

However, not all receptors respond in this way, as can be seen in Figure 2.20, which illustrates the action potential responses evoked by mechanical stimulation of two different receptors.

○   What differences are evident between the two responses?

●   The firing from the receptor in Figure 2.20a is maintained throughout the stimulus period, although the frequency declines slowly with time. However, in the receptor shown in Figure 2.20b, the firing rate subsides rapidly, and it only fires during the period when the stimulus is increasing; it does not respond to a steady stimulus.

This decline in the action potential firing rate of a receptor during a steady stimulus is called **sensory adaptation**. Different receptors display different and characteristic

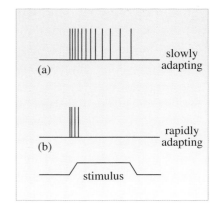

Figure 2.20   Adaptation of receptors to a stimulus that is gradually applied and then held constant before gradually decreasing. (a) Slowly adapting receptor. (b) Rapidly adapting receptor.

rates of adaptation. No receptor displays a perfectly regular discharge. Receptors such as that shown in Figure 2.20a are *slowly adapting*. Figure 2.20b shows an example of a *rapidly adapting receptor*.

○   What function might adaptation serve?

●   It will reduce the amount of neural activity reaching the spinal cord, so that the central nervous system (CNS) is not continuously bombarded with inputs about unchanging stimuli. Can you imagine what it would be like if you were aware of your clothes all the time?

To illustrate the rapid adaptation of the hair-follicle receptors, use a pencil tip to move a hair on your arm and hold it in the new position, without touching the skin surface. (Even better, get someone else to do this for you.) Try this several times, with different speeds and directions of movements. You will be aware of the hair's movement, but not when it is held stationary.

If you close your eyes and can get someone else to do the exercise above you will find that you can locate the position of the stimulus. We are now going to show how this is achieved.

2.2.3 Sensory input to the spinal cord and brain

The information about the signal that is transduced by receptors is transferred to the CNS as action potentials, along afferent neurons. Sensory inflow from the body (below the neck) occurs via peripheral nerves that run from each part of the body to the spinal cord (Figures 2.1 and 2.21). At this point the peripheral nerve is called a spinal nerve.

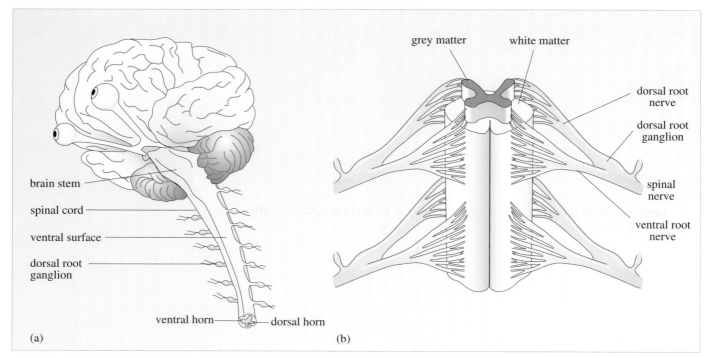

Figure 2.21   (a) The human brain and upper part of the spinal cord showing the location of the brainstem. (b) A length of spinal cord normally lying within two vertebrae showing the characteristic grey and white matter. Note the bilaterally symmetrical arrangement of the pairs of dorsal root (sensory) and ventral root (motor) nerves. Together these constitute what is known as a spinal nerve. Note also the dorsal root ganglion, where the cell bodies of the neurons that make up the dorsal root nerve are situated.

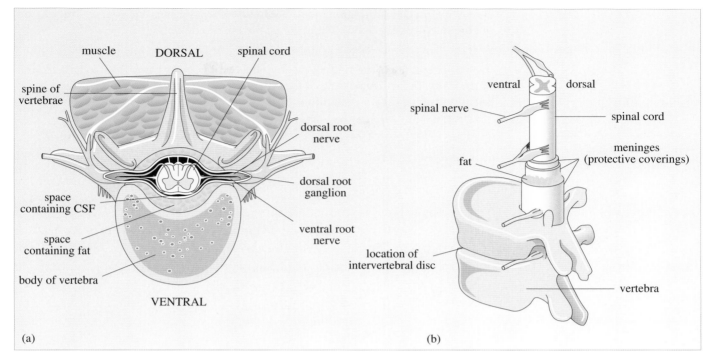

Figure 2.22   (a) Transverse section through the spinal cord. (b) Diagram showing the structure of the spinal cord and its associated peripheral (spinal) nerves, in a section of the vertebral column.

○   What is the difference between a nerve and a neuron?

●   The term 'nerve' refers to bundles of axons located together; 'neuron' refers to a single cell.

You will have noticed that the nerves are not arranged continuously along the length of the spinal cord but are bundled together in pairs, one on the left and one on the right. One left/right pair emerges from within each of the vertebrae that form the backbone. The sensory inflow from your body to the spinal cord is organized on a segmental basis corresponding to the spinal column vertebrae, as shown in Figure 2.22.

Within the peripheral nerve there are hundreds of axons. You can see that the peripheral nerve divides just before entering the spinal cord. The dorsal nerve contains only sensory (afferent) axons and is known as the **dorsal root**. The ventral nerve contains motor (efferent) axons and is called the ventral root. All the cell bodies of the sensory neurons are found outside the spinal cord in enlargements of the dorsal roots called the **dorsal root ganglia** (also shown in Figures 2.21 and 2.22).

○   Look again at Figure 2.18 and say where the cell body of mechanoreceptors, such as the hair receptor or Meissner's corpuscle will be found.

●   These mechanoreceptors are modified sensory neurons so their cell bodies will be in the dorsal root ganglia.

The sensory inflow to the spinal cord, via the dorsal root ganglia, not only conveys information about deformation of the skin (touch and pressure) but also temperature, noxious stimuli, tissue damage, joint position and movement as well as the state of muscle stretch. In other words, the axons of the sensory neurons responsible for conveying touch information (such as Meissner's corpuscles and Merkel's discs) are not the only sensory axons that make up the peripheral nerve.

If we investigate the source of the axons of touch sensitive receptors that make up one peripheral nerve we find that all the sensory receptors come from a defined area of the body. In fact the surface of the body can be divided into areas called **dermatomes** as shown in Figure 2.23.

Figure 2.23 A schematic illustration of body surface zones or dermatomes.

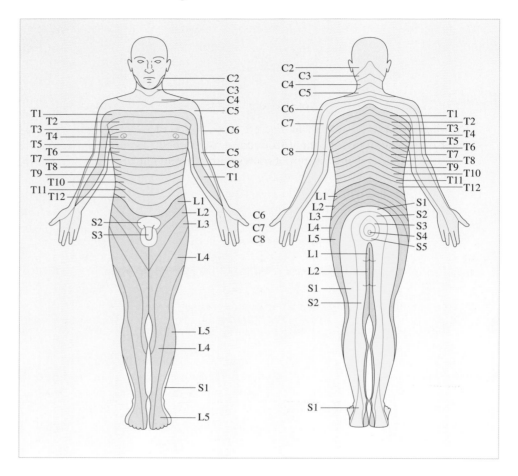

The sensory receptors from one dermatome feed information via one peripheral nerve into one dorsal root and thence into one segment of the spinal cord (see Figure 2.17). Thus tactile information carried into the spinal cord by axons in the 4th lumbar nerve (L4) has arisen from a stimulus falling somewhere in the L4 dermatome.

○   Look at Figure 2.23. How helpful would it be to you, in pinpointing a stimulus locality, to know that activity was being observed in an axon from the right dorsal root of L4?

●   Not very!

The stimulus might be from anywhere on a strip of skin starting across the lower back and extending round the right hip and down the right leg to the big toe. In fact, the recording is even less informative than that on two counts. Firstly, although our diagram in Figure 2.23 shows the dermatomes as discrete areas, there is a lot of 'fuzziness' at the borders between dermatomes. A touch stimulus near the border of

L4 and L5 could result in activity being detected in some axons in the dorsal roots of both the associated lumbar spinal nerves. Secondly, as just mentioned, the sensory inflow to the spinal cord via the dorsal roots, does not only convey information about touch. It also contains the sensory axons from receptors that respond to temperature, pressure, tissue damage, joint position and movement as well as the state of muscle stretch, as shown in Figure 2.24. We will study these other receptors in more detail in Block 5 of this course.

Figure 2.24 is obviously a stylised diagram of the arrangement for incoming somatic sensory information to the spinal cord but it does give a clue to the way that the brain might be able to determine whether a train of action potentials were signalling touch rather than temperature.

○ From Figure 2.24 what can you see to be happening in the spinal cord?

● The diagram shows a number of discrete arrows ascending in the spinal cord thereby suggesting that the input from the sensory dorsal root diverges and that there are a number of different routes within the spinal cord, all ascending to the brain.

These arrows represent different pathways. One way of indicating the sensory modality is to have all information from that modality kept separate from other modalities and finally terminate in a specific region of the brain. This is known as the **labelled line code**. This is exactly what happens for touch. The axons of the mechanoreceptors enter the spinal cord, together with the other sensory axons that make up the dorsal root of the spinal nerve, and then the axons from the cells specialized for touch reception segregate away from the other axons, and ascend the spinal cord, until they reach the area of the brain known as the **brainstem**, where they terminate in a specific area, the **medulla** (also known as the *medulla oblongata*).

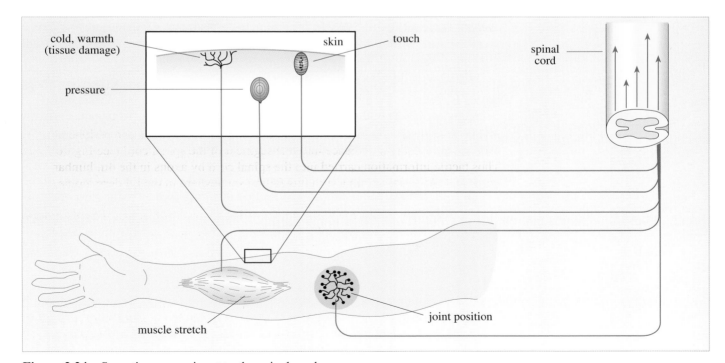

Figure 2.24   Somatic sensory input to the spinal cord.

Figure 2.25 A cross-section of spinal cord taken from the upper part of the body showing the ascending tracts of the spinal cord white matter.

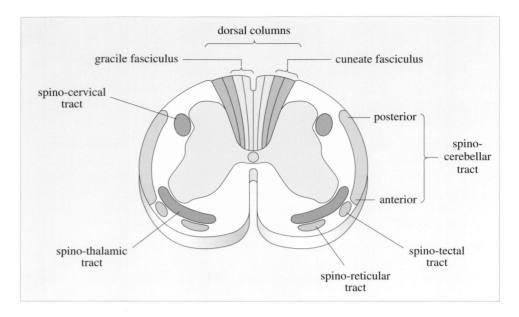

They ascend, tightly packed together, in discernible bundles that are called the **dorsal columns** and these can be clearly seen in a cross-section of the spinal cord (Figure 2.25). They are whitish in appearance because all these axons are myelinated.

In fact, the dorsal columns comprise two bundles of sensory axons or, to use classical anatomical terminology, *fasciculi*. These are the *gracile fasciculi* and the *cuneate fasciculi*. The axons forming the cuneate fasciculi originate from cells that have their cell bodies in the dorsal root ganglia of the cervical and thoracic spinal nerves (i.e. they bring in touch information from the upper part of the body). In the medulla, where they terminate, they make synaptic contact with neurons in the *cuneate nucleus* (Figure 2.26). In relation to brain anatomy, the term '**nucleus**' is used to denote an area where many neurons are synapsing.

Axons from the gracile fasciculus originate from sensory neurons that enter the spinal cord by the dorsal roots of the lumbar and sacral spinal nerves (i.e. they bring tactile information from the dermatomes of the lower body.) Axons of the gracile fasciculus terminate in the *gracile nucleus* of the medulla, making synaptic contact with neurons in the gracile nucleus. The cuneate nucleus and gracile nucleus are together known as the **dorsal column nuclei (DCN)**.

○ Figure 2.25 shows a cross-section of spinal cord taken from the upper part of the body. If you were to sketch a cross-section of spinal cord from the lower part of the body how would it differ from Figure 2.25?

● There would be no cuneate fasciculus. You might also surmise (correctly) that the circumference of the cross-section would be smaller because there would be fewer ascending axons.

Examination of the spinal cord at different levels reveals that the positions of the axons are conserved as they ascend. The axons from the lower part of the body are found toward the centre of the dorsal columns and, as each spinal nerve feeds into the column, its axons are added laterally. Seeing how the information from spatially adjoining areas is added into the pathway whilst maintaining an equivalent spatial

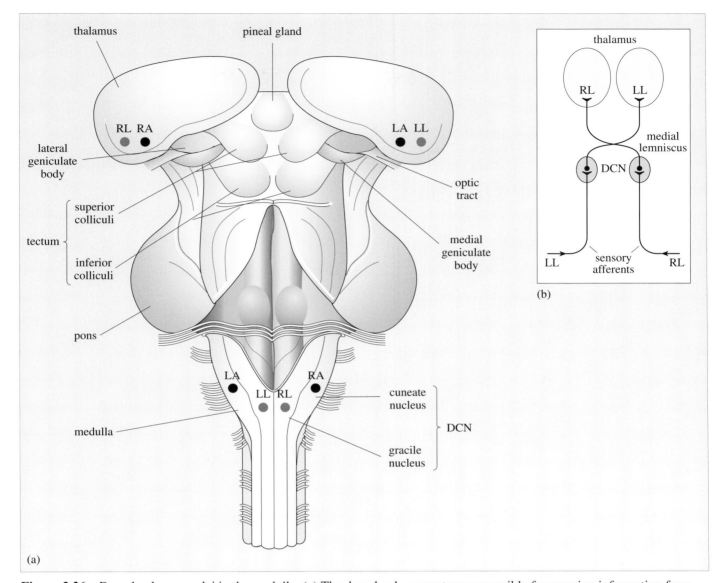

Figure 2.26   Dorsal column nuclei in the medulla. (a) The dorsal column system responsible for carrying information from sensory neurons to the medulla. The red and black dots indicate the neural inputs from the limbs that are transported via the gracile and cuneate bundles and terminate on opposite sides of the thalamus. (b) A schematic diagram of the sensory pathways of the system to show the cross-over pathways involved. LA = left arm, LL = left leg, RA = right arm, RL = right leg.

arrangement within the pathway gives us a final clue about the method that is used to indicate the precise location of a tactile stimulus.

Neurons that lie close to one another in the DCN have receptive fields that are also close together. In this way, the entire body surface is represented in an orderly way in the DCN. The top part of the body is systematically represented in the cuneate nuclei, and the lower part in the gracile nuclei. Thus, in these nuclei, the entire body surface is represented in the regular arrangement of many thousands of little 'windows' each of which corresponds to a single neuron, and each of which 'looks' at a very small part of the body surface, i.e. that cell's receptive field. This maintenance of the spatial relationships between adjacent areas of skin or **topographic representation** (topographic = map-like) in the DCN, is known as a *somatotopic organization*.

Furthermore, it is maintained in a general way, as each pathway proceeds from the DCN by way of a tract called the *medial lemniscus*, which crosses over to the opposite (*contralateral*) side of the brain, and terminates in another brain structure, the **thalamus** (Figure 2.26). The thalamus is a large forebrain structure (see Figure 2.27a and b) which is an important relay centre for many kinds of incoming sensory information. Tactile information (mechanoreceptor) inputs to the ventro-posterior lateral (VPL) nucleus, which is part of the **ventrobasal nucleus** (**VBN**), as does proprioceptive information. Visual information feeds into the **lateral geniculate nucleus**, auditory into the **medial geniculate nucleus**. There are also non-specific areas. Some thalamic nuclei have functions in motor (movement) control systems, that is input is from other brain areas where 'decisions' to execute actions have already been taken.

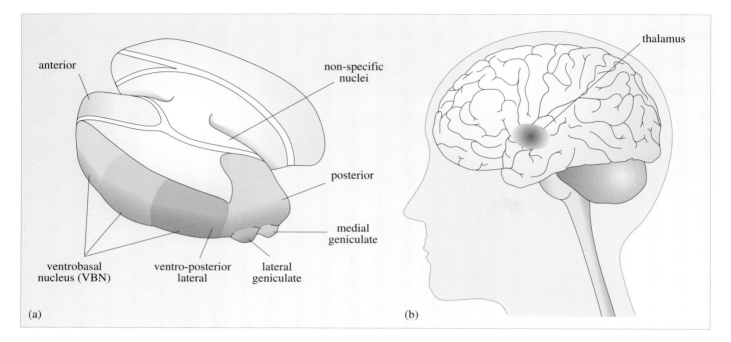

Figure 2.27 (a) The sub-divisions of the thalamus. (b) The location of the thalamus within the brain.

○ Although we are only concerned with following the pathway of tactile information from skin to brain at the moment, what does this extra information about the thalamus suggest to you concerning the *function* of the thalamus?

● It is not just a relay station for the incoming information, which is on its way to other brain structures. The fact that there is input from areas where processing of incoming information has already taken place and an outcome has been 'decided' suggests that there could be potential to modify incoming signals here. The thalamus may therefore be an information processing centre in its own right.

Although we shall ignore this for the moment, we should bear it in mind because the thalamus will be discussed in several other parts of the course.

The face has its own separate somatosensory system. It is in the VBN that tactile information from the face inputs from the fifth (Vth) cranial nerve (trigeminal nerve). The strict somatotopic organization is seen here too, and is maintained as axons project from the thalamus to the cortex of the brain (see Figure 2.28).

The final destination of the tactile pathway is the **primary somatosensory cortex**.

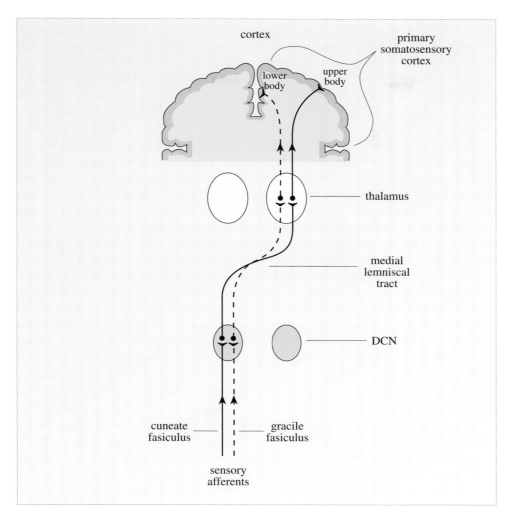

Figure 2.28   Axonal projections from thalamus to somatosensory cortex.

Here the receptive fields of the neurons, whilst still being topographically arranged are at first sight bizarre. The amount of cortical tissue devoted to each region does not relate to the physical size of the region but to its sensitivity (Figure 2.29 overleaf and Box 2.3, p.107).

Those parts of the body, such as the fingers and the lips, that have the largest representation in the primary somatosensory cortex relative to size, have more sensory neurons per unit area of surface, than say the legs or trunk. Furthermore, in these regions where there are more sensory neurons per unit area, the receptive fields also tend to be smaller.

These differences in **innervation** (the distribution of nerves to an organ) have functional implications. The regions of the body that have the greatest density of neurons and the greatest cortical representation are those parts of the body that have the best powers of discrimination. For example, you can probably put your hand into a pocket or purse and bring out a particular coin without having to look at it. This ability to recognize the shape of an object by touch alone is called *stereognosis*. The use of Braille 'letters' by the visually impaired is also made possible by the dense innervation of the fingers and the resultant high degree of spatial discrimination. To convey similar meaning, Braille characters would have to be many times larger, if people had to use the skin on their forearms instead of fingertips to read them.

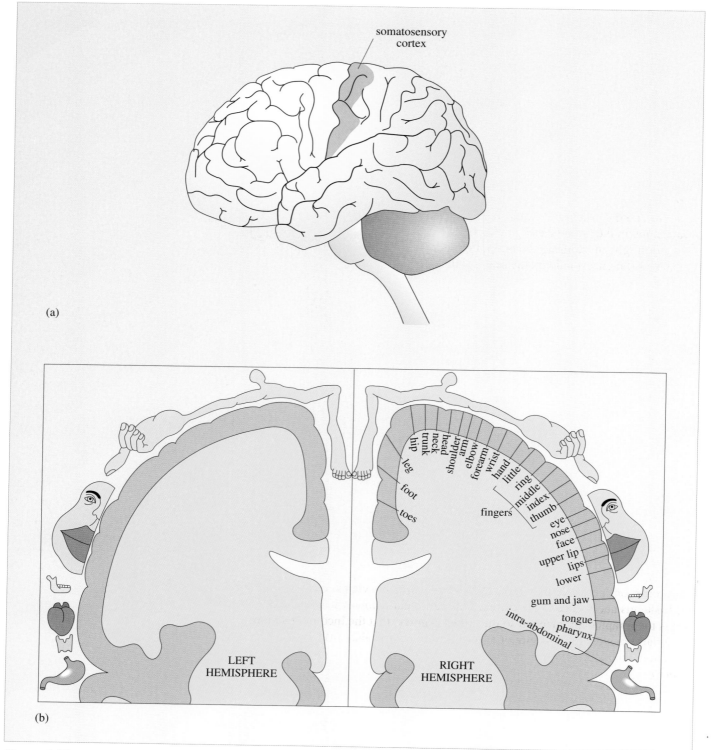

Figure 2.29 (a) The somatosensory area of the brain. (b) The sensory homunculus.

Box 2.3   The mapping of the human somatosensory cortex

Before carrying out surgery to remove cortical tissue from patients suffering from epilepsy or tumours, the Canadian neurosurgeon the late Wilder Penfield (1891–1976) explored affected and also adjacent regions of the cerebral cortex by stimulating them electrically. There are no sensory receptors in cortical tissues; the only structures beneath the skull that produce any sensation are the three membranes, the *dura mater*, the *pia mater* and the *arachnoid mater*, that surround and contain the brain (see Figure 2.16). Accordingly, in exposing the brain, Penfield used a local anaesthetic on the scalp, skull and membranes. The patient could then be conscious to report any experiences resulting from direct electrical stimulation of the brain without suffering any pain or discomfort.

Penfield assessed the potential effect of removing cortical tissue by observing the patients' behaviour or by asking the patient to report any experiences that occurred during the electrical stimulation. If stimulation of a region of cortex produced no effect on the patients' behaviour, the assumption was that it could be removed without any serious consequences to the patient. It was only after this confirmation that he carried out his operations.

In this way the primary sensory region of the human cortex first came to be mapped.

So does this complete our study of the sense of touch? We have shown that information from a distal object (say, a feather) provides a proximal mechanical stimulus (light touch) as it brushes against our skin (*quality*). The pressure is transduced by the mechanoreceptor, generating first a receptor potential and then action potentials. The pattern of action potentials can code for the stimulus *intensity* and *duration*, and intensity can also be conveyed by the number of receptors that respond. There is an anatomical pathway from the skin receptor to the primary somatosensory cortex of the brain. The pathway projects via the dorsal columns to the thalamus and thence to the cortex. This particular pathway is specific to touch and is topographically mapped so the cortex 'knows' that the incoming action potentials are signalling receipt of a touch sensation and also, from the position on the cortex where the activity is received, from whence the stimulus originated (*location*). This description would strongly support Gibson's model of direct perception (Section 2.2.1). Yet our *perception* of a touch stimulus immediately raises some problems for this model. The way that a stimulus is perceived relates strongly to whether we touch or are touched.

2.2.4   The perception of touch

In Block 1 your attention was drawn to the fact that touching and being touched are very important activities in our sexual and emotional lives. In this section we will take a brief look at much simpler situations. For example, in the previous section we remarked on our ability to distinguish between different coins using only our fingers.

Activity 2.2

Try this for yourself now. Take several different coins and put them in a bag. Decide which one you will select first and which one second. Try to describe how exactly you came to make your choice. Did you select accurately or not? You can also ask another person to do this for you. How did you (or they) describe the process of choosing the coin?

In this activity you probably did something like feeling around the edge of the coin, maybe you palpated it (a sort of squeeze) or hefted it ('throwing' it up and down in your hand without losing hold of it). These actions can be described as *active touch*.

Activity 2.3

This activity is much better if you can work with another person, but you can get some idea of the different perception you gain if you place one hand comfortably on the table, palm up with your thumb close enough to your finger so that a coin can be rubbed between fingers and thumb (Figure 2.30). Lay several different coins on the table in front of you, close your eyes and mix them around with your free hand. Then, eyes still closed take one and move it over to your immobile other hand and rub it between the motionless fingers and thumb. Can your immobile hand identify the coin?

In this activity, your inert fingers are being touched and this is described as *passive* touch. If you had to do this on your own, your moving hand probably 'knows' what coin it picks up so this is a bit tricky to simulate! However, it should have given you some feel for the different perception generated by passive touch.

Figure 2.30   An example of passive touch.

You probably also know that a light touch to the sole of your foot generates a perception of 'tickle' if applied by someone other than yourself. It is impossible to generate the same perception by self-stimulation. The reason for this seems to reside in the total predictability of self-stimulation. Commands from your own brain generate the motor (muscular) activity that results in the light touch being applied in a particular way to the chosen area of skin. This can be studied experimentally using an apparatus that delivers a consistent stimulus to the sole of the foot and can be operated by the experimenter or by the *subject* (person being studied). The stimulus is perceived as ticklish when the experimenter operates the 'tickle box' and far less tickly when the subject is in control. Intermediate results were obtained when the box was set up so that the experimenter actually controlled the movement but the subject's hand was on the device and passively moved as it would if they were directing the stimulus.

The perception of tickle cannot simply be attributed to the unpredictability of the stimulus, because we know that the perception can occur in the *absence* of the *adequate stimulus* (touch in this case). If you are very ticklish you will know that the perception can be generated by someone wriggling their fingers and saying something like, 'I'm coming to tickle you', just as mention of a lemon can cause many of us to salivate.

What is going on here? Can neurobiology throw any further light on how we perceive touch stimuli? The next section takes up this challenge.

Summary of Section 2.2

Sensory receptors are the interface between events in the environment and the rest of the nervous system. A sensory receptor responds to its own adequate stimulus by generating a receptor potential. The receptor is said to transduce the stimulus energy into electrical activity.

Using the sense of touch as our example we have shown how various properties of the sensory signal can be coded for by the nervous system. The quality of the stimulus, by which we mean the fact that the stimulus is a light touch, not a sound or a taste, is specified by the receptor that is responding. All receptors of a specific type communicate (via pathways involving other neurons) with specific areas of the cerebral cortex. Activity in the somatosensory cortex will indicate a touch stimulus, in the auditory cortex, sound, and in the visual cortex, sight (Block 1, Figure 5.2).

The duration of a stimulus may be conveyed by a receptor responding continuously throughout the whole period of the stimulus presentation. But very often the receptor only responds at the beginning of a stimulus being presented. In other words, the receptor responds to change in the stimulus environment. This property of the receptor is known as adaptation and specific receptors have typical rates at which they adapt.

The intensity of the stimulus can be coded by the size of the receptor potential. In the case of touch receptors this converts immediately into the rate of firing or frequency of action potentials because the sensory receptors are modified sensory neurons. Also, with touch receptors the intensity of the stimulus will affect how many receptors respond. A light touch will recruit more receptors than one that is barely perceptible. But the relationship between the number of receptors recruited and the intensity of stimulation will depend upon which part of the body surface is touched because some areas, for example the fingers, have more receptors per unit area than other areas, for example the back.

The precise location of the stimulus can be ascertained because there are specific pathways from the surface of the skin connected via synaptic relay centres to specific areas of the somatosensory cortex. The whole surface of the skin is topographically mapped in the somatosensory cortex. The skin areas are known as dermatomes and the most sensitive areas of the body have more space devoted to them giving rise to the bizarre sensory homunculus.

This account appears to support Gibson's model of direct perception but this is at odds with the fact that the perception of touch depends on whether you touch or are touched.

Question 2.4

The Brown-Sequard syndrome results from a specific spinal cord injury in which all the tracts on one side of the cord are cut through, leaving those on the other side intact. Such a lesion in the cervical part of the cord will affect touch sensations from the arms. From your knowledge of the spinal cord pathways, predict the effect on bodily tactile sensation that might result from a lesion through the *right* side of the spinal cord in the cervical region.

2.3 Neuronal processing

2.3.1 Pathways in the spinal cord and brain

When following the path of the axon from the touch receptor into the spinal cord and up the dorsal columns to the medulla, we ignored the fact that anatomical studies show the axons branching soon after they enter the spinal cord (Figure 2.31).

Figure 2.31 Cross-section of the spinal cord showing branching of an axon from a mechanoreceptor (sensory afferent from a sense organ) in the grey matter. The grey matter looks greyish because there are a lot of cell bodies there, the white matter looks whitish because it transects tracts of axons going up or down the spinal cord and the axons are covered in myelin.

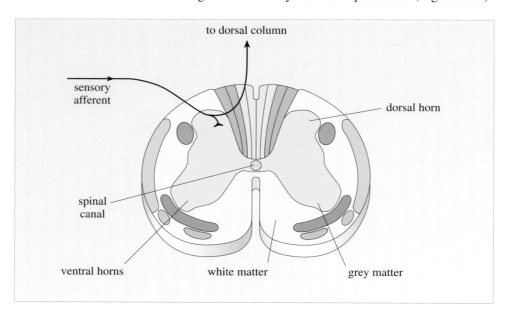

One of the branches remains at that level of the spinal cord and enters the **grey matter** where it makes synaptic contact with other neurons some of which then relay the signals to the brain via ascending pathways in addition to the dorsal column pathway. One of these, and a major pathway into which the axons from the touch receptors feed, is the spino-cervical pathway (sometimes called the spino-cervical-thalamic tract) (Figure 2.32). The axons of this pathway synapse in the cervical nucleus (in the region of the neck). From here the pathway merges with the medial lemniscal tract.

○ Where will this pathway go next?

● Having merged with the medial lemniscal tract it will project to the thalamus.

   In fact it goes to the same locality within the thalamus.

○ Where will this be?

● The VPL area within the VBN.

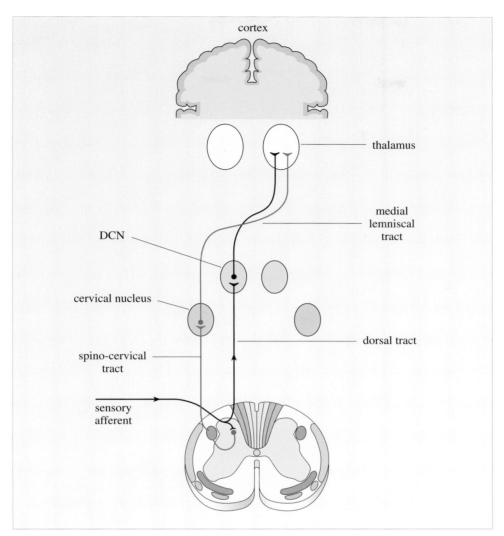

Figure 2.32   The dorsal column and the spinocervical pathways.

Where the sensory branches do not synapse with neurons that feed into the ascending pathways they are involved in local circuits that control reflex responses, such as the rapid removal of a limb from the source of any unexpected touch stimulus (Figure 2.33 overleaf).

The dorsal column medial lemniscal (DCML) and the spino-cervical tracts (SCT) are known as *specific* pathways as the information coded by the receptors is preserved and accurately transmitted at successive synapses. It is information carried by the pathways that allows us to accurately locate, for example, a biting insect on our leg. The nuclei to which the DCML and SCT project in the thalamus are known as the *specific thalamic nuclei*. However, there are also *non-specific* pathways, where there is considerable convergence of inputs from different modalities. Through links made in the grey matter, tactile information flows into these ascending pathways, one of which is the spino-reticular pathway (Figure 2.34 overleaf). In pathways such as this, the detailed information coded by the receptors is lost and the reticular pathways probably function to alert us to activity in our environment in some rather general way. Thus a light touch could awaken you from sleep but leave you unsure as to what had woken you.

Figure 2.33 Diagram of local circuit neurons controlling limb movement in response to unexpected touch stimulus.

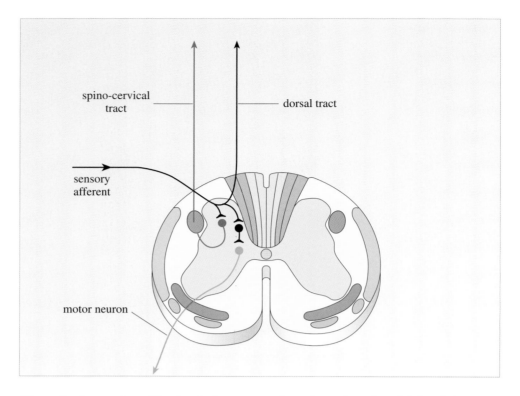

The **reticular system**, like the thalamus, consists of a series of nuclei, but it is a more diffuse structure which extends from the medulla to the midbrain. There are pathways from this reticular formation to various areas of the cortex and to the *non-specific* thalamic nuclei (Figures 2.34 and Figure 2.27).

Now that we have looked more closely at the variety of routes that touch information flows along, we observe that the signal is not just sent directly to the primary somatosensory cortex without opportunity for modification. We need to look in more detail at the neuronal circuitry and at the receptive fields of the cells along the specific pathway of the DCML tract, firstly to find out what, if any, processing takes place between the receptors and the somatosensory cortex because, although the information is preserved and accurately transmitted, some areas of skin are more sensitive than others.

2.3.2 Neuronal circuitry and receptive fields

Mechanoreceptors

You have already undertaken an activity to establish that some parts of the body are particularly well able to discriminate between two discrete stimuli on the surface of your skin. The fingertips are especially sensitive. In Block 1 this was attributed to there being a high density of receptors in that area.

○ Can you think of any other requirements that would enable the nervous system to detect two separate stimuli placed very close to one another? (Hint: Figure 2.35 overleaf may be helpful, and remember also that our diagrams are two-dimensional representations of three-dimensional objects.)

● Each receptor would need to gather information from a very small area (its receptive field) which did not overlap with the receptive fields of neighbouring receptors.

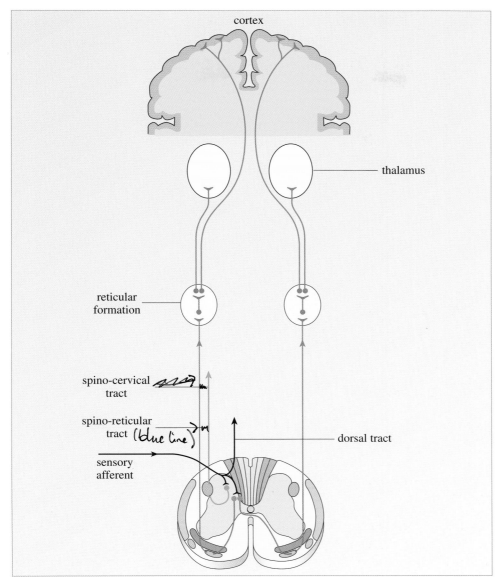

Figure 2.34   The spino-reticular pathway.

Figure 2.35a (overleaf) shows diagrammatically the kind of arrangement we would expect to find below the skin surface of the fingertips. In fact, when recordings have been made from individual dorsal root ganglion cells, using the experimental arrangement shown in Figure 2.19, results are as shown in Figure 2.36 (overleaf). There is almost no overlapping of receptive fields in the fingers. There is also, as you would expect, somatotopic mapping. Adjacent sensory axons have adjacent receptive fields.

○   What do you notice about the receptive fields of dorsal root ganglion cells (i.e. mechanoreceptors) transducing tactile stimuli from the palm and forearm?

●   These receptive fields are much larger than those found in the fingers and they overlap with fields of other cells.

Figure 2.35 Diagram showing endings of sensory neurons and how they provide receptive field properties. (a) Three non-overlapping receptive fields provided by three sensory neurons, A, B and C. Simultaneous stimulation at points 1 and 2 can be discriminated. (b) Two overlapping receptive fields provided by two neurons, D and E. Simultaneous stimulation at points 3 and 4 cannot be discriminated.

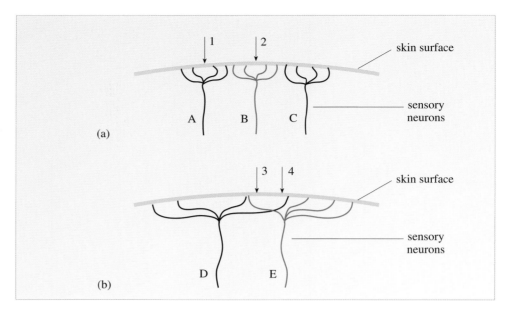

Figure 2.36 Typical receptive field sizes of dorsal root ganglion cells with receptive fields in the forearm, palm and fingers.

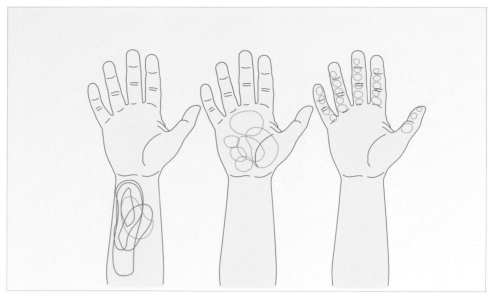

○   What is the functional consequence of this?

●   A tactile stimulus on a piece of skin in these areas will excite several mechanoreceptors (or dorsal root ganglion cells) and a second, nearby, stimulus might excite the same group of cells. Thus it would be impossible to say that there were two distinct stimuli. (Figure 2.35b shows this situation diagrammatically.)

Cortical response to mechanoreceptor stimulation

We have already described how axons from the tactile mechanoreceptors ascend toward the brain as the dorsal column tracts, and make their first synapse in dorsal column nuclei of the medulla. Specifically, the axons from the mechanoreceptors in the hands and arms will synapse onto cells in the cuneate nucleus (Figure 2.26). So the next neurons in this specific pathway are those that project from the dorsal column nuclei (DCN) of the medulla to the thalamic nuclei on the opposite side of the body (that is, the *contralateral* thalamic nuclei). These *second order* neurons – typically, the second neuron in an afferent pathway is called a second order neuron – project contralaterally to the VPL nucleus of the thalamus. It is at the synapse of the receptors with the second order neurons that *divergence* first occurs in this pathway. You may recall that at the beginning of Section 2 it was stated that each neuron in the brain could have several thousand inputs and outputs (Figures 2.6 and 2.10). By divergence of output one receptor can influence a large population of DCN cells and progressively larger populations of thalamic and, finally, cortical cells as shown in Figure 2.37.

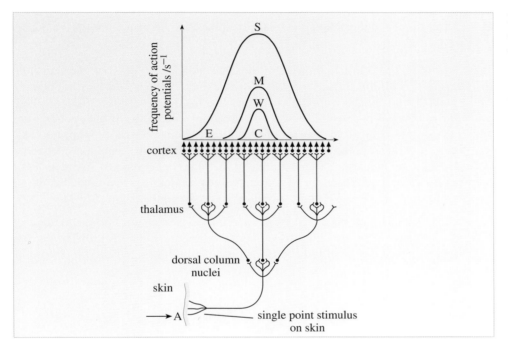

Figure 2.37   Diagram showing divergence in the neuronal circuitry conveying tactile stimulation from a pinpoint on the skin surface to the somatosensory cortex. The curves indicate the firing frequency of action potentials of cortical neurons in response to stimulation of the skin at point A. S = strong stimulus, M = medium stimulus, W = weak stimulus. Areas labelled E and C are discussed in the text.

○   Consider the sensory homunculus (Figure 2.29b) and say whether you would expect there to be most divergence in the pathway from finger to cortex or forearm to cortex.

●   There is a relatively larger area of cortex devoted to the fingers so you would expect that these pathways show the greater divergence.

To keep our investigation as simple as possible the diagram shows each second order and subsequent neuron in the pathway as receiving input from only one neuron; in reality not only does each cell have thousands of outputs, there are also thousands of inputs to be integrated. The consequence of this will become clear when we study the receptive field properties of the cortical cells in this and in subsequent blocks. Meantime, we will continue to explore the effect of the rather artificial experimental situation where we have only one single point stimulus falling on the skin. From Figure 2.37 you can see that although this stimulus can have an effect on a large area of somatosensory cortex, it does not influence the whole area in a homogeneous fashion.

○ What is the effect of a weak stimulus (W) falling on the skin at A for a cortical cell from area C? And for area E?

● When A is weakly stimulated cortical cells in area C will fire, but those in area E will not.

○ What will cause cortical cells in area E to respond?

● A stronger stimulus falling on the skin area A will cause cortical cells in area E to fire.

○ If you were recording from a cortical cell in area C, how would you be able to distinguish between a strong and a weak stimulus on the skin at A?

● The frequency of the action potentials, or spikes, would be greater for the stronger stimulus.

Look now at Figure 2.38a. If we were to stimulate an adjacent point on the skin and then look for activity in cells of the somatosensory cortex we would find that many of the cells that responded were the same ones that had responded when our original point A was being stimulated. The expectation would then be that if both points were simultaneously stimulated the pattern of activity across the cortical cells would not look very different from the activity produced by a single point stimulation. Indeed, if the effect of the two inputs were additive, it might be rather hard to distinguish between the activity produced by one strong point stimulus, and that produced by two simultaneously presented point stimuli of lesser strength (Figure 2.38b).

However, the actual pattern of activity recorded when two adjacent points in the fingertips are simultaneously stimulated is quite different. (Figure 2.38c) The pattern of activity shows two distinct peaks enabling a very clear judgement to be made distinguishing between the effect of these two stimuli being applied to the skin. (Figure 2.38c) and only one stimulus being applied (Figure 2.37).

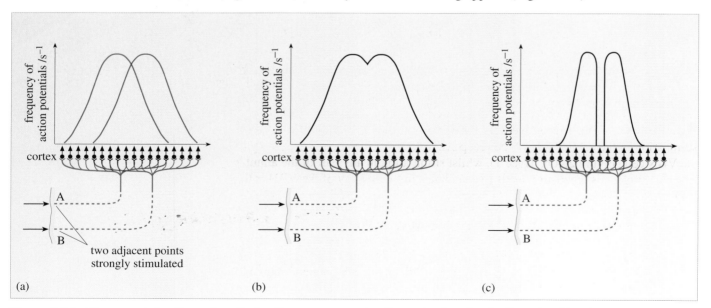

Figure 2.38   The expected pattern of cortical cell responses to stimuli at point A and point B on the skin when (a) stimulation is not simultaneous, (b) stimulation is simultaneous. (c) The pattern of activity across the region of cortex influenced by stimulation at A and B, when A and B are stimulated simultaneously.

The cause of this dramatic cortical response is the result of a phenomenon that is found widely in the sensory nervous system: **lateral inhibition**.

Lateral inhibition

One way to send a very clear, sharp signal is to inhibit any other surrounding 'noise', or message. Neurons in afferent pathways do this quite literally. A neuron that is stimulated can excite the next neuron in the ascending sensory pathway and at the same time send inhibitory signals to neighbouring neurons within that sensory modality. These lateral inhibitory signals are found in virtually every sensory pathway in the human nervous system. In the case of the dorsal column medial lemniscal (DCML) pathway, there is a lateral inhibition at every synaptic level. Figure 2.39 shows how this might be brought about.

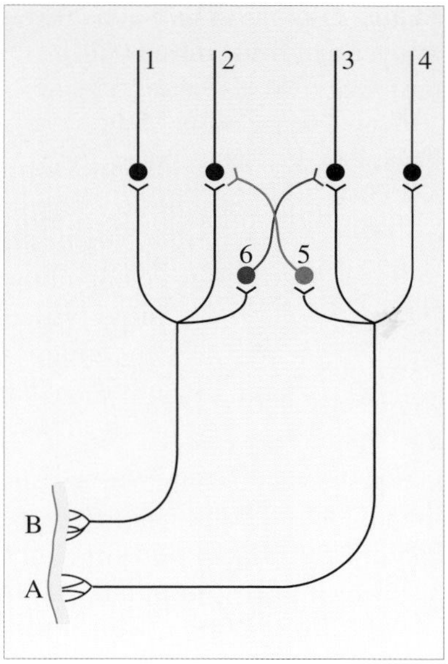

If you look at Figure 2.39 you can see that the stimulus at A would excite cells 3 and 4 which project from the DCN to the thalamus. Cell 5 is also excited but this is a small neuron that terminates, still within the DCN, onto cell 2 in an inhibitory fashion. In the same way if only B is stimulated, cells 1 and 2 and the inhibitory cell 6 are excited.

Figure 2.39   Schematic diagram to illustrate lateral inhibition at the cellular level.

○   Which of cells 1, 2, 3 and 4 will be excited if A and B are stimulated at the same time?

●   Only 1 and 4 because the stimulation of 2 and 3 is cancelled by the inhibition from 5 and 6.

Although this is obviously very simplified, it is the basis of lateral inhibition. Incidentally, there are many small neurons in the brain and spinal cord like cells 5 and 6. Some are inhibitory, others excitatory, but they all allow for complex processing of incoming (and outgoing) information in the nervous system. They are called **interneurons**.

So what actually happens if we record from cells in the DCML pathway?

Recordings from a single neuron in the VPL area of the VBN, show that the neuron has a regular rate of firing in the absence of any stimulation. Interestingly, this is true of many neurons and is known as the **background firing rate**. The receptive field of a single neuron can be mapped on the surface of the skin, by lightly touching the skin with a fine pointed object, or tiny puff of air. If the VBN cell shows any *change* in response then the stimulus lies within the cell's receptive field on the skin. Figure 2.40a shows the receptive field for one cell in the VBN. Notice that stimulation in the central area of the receptive field results in *increased* activity in the VBN cell (Figure 2.40b, Trace 1), whilst stimulation in any part of the annular ring that surrounds the centre, leads to a *decrease* in the activity of the VBN cell (Figure 2.40b, Trace 2).

○   How would you explain this effect on the activity of the VBN cell?

●   When the receptor(s) under the skin in the area of the annular ring (shown as triangles) are stimulated they must activate inhibitory pathways that link to the VBN cell from which we are recording.

Notice that in Trace 1 the increase in frequency of firing following the application of the touch stimulus is almost immediate. In Trace 2 the inhibition occurs following a slight latency.

Figure 2.40 (a) The concentrically organized receptive field of neuron A in the VPL area of the VBN of the thalamus. (b) The responses of a VBN neuron to tactile stimulation. Trace 1 shows the response when the stimulus is applied to the centre of the field for a period shown as t_1. Trace 2 shows the response when the stimulus is applied anywhere in the outer annulus for the same period of t_1 and Trace 3 shows the simultaneous stimulation of both regions.

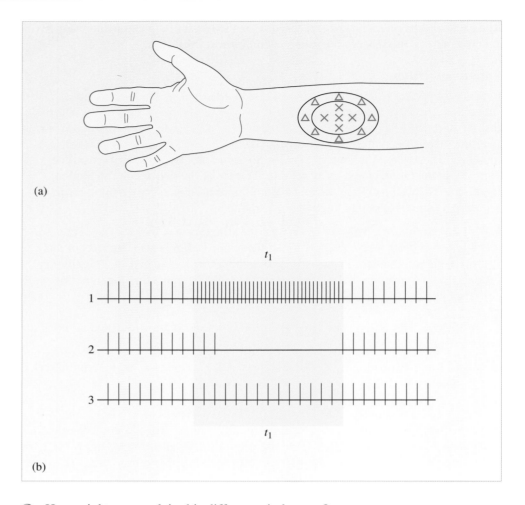

(a)

(b)

○ How might you explain this difference in latency?

● You might think that if a longer route was involved the information would take longer to reach the target cell. You might wonder whether the speed of conduction of action potentials was slower along the inhibitory pathway (Table 2.2). But in this particular case the reason is that there are additional chemical synapses in the pathway and this adds the extra delay (Section 2.1.1).

The type of arrangement that will give rise to the results obtained by this recording is shown schematically in Figure 2.41.

○ Whilst recording from neuron A in Figure 2.41, what would be the effect of stimulating the centre region of the receptive field for A in the forearm?

● The receptor (represented by a cross) would be stimulated and action potentials will be generated in the axon that terminates in the DCN. The diagram shows this to result in an excitatory input to cell A which will therefore increase its rate of firing (see also Figure 2.40b, Trace 1.)

○ What would be observed if recording from neuron B whilst applying the stimulus to the outer region of cell A's receptive field?

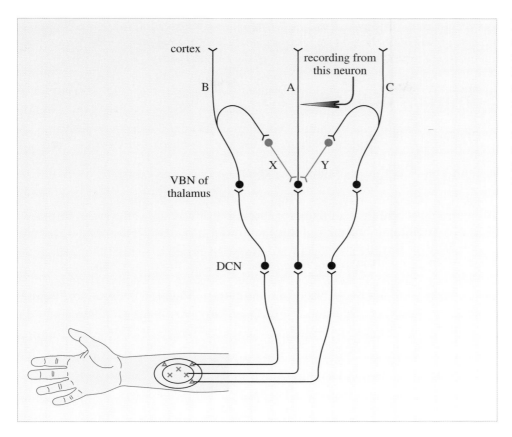

Figure 2.41   The receptive field of cell A is shown located on the forearm. This diagram gives a hypothetical basis of the complex, concentrically organized receptive field of cell A (which is itself located in the thalamus). These types of synaptic connections could account for the observed properties of complex receptive fields of thalamic neurons.

●   The receptor (represented by a triangle), would be stimulated and there would then be a similar sequence of events leading to the excitation of neuron B with the same time course as shown for neuron A. (Note that the same would apply to neuron C.)

○   In this event, how would the activity recorded at A change?

●   Our diagram shows an inhibitory interneuron, X, that links between neurons B and A. Activity in B stimulates the interneuron X, which in turn inhibits activity in A. The reduction in activity in A will be seen slightly later than the increased activity in B because of the synaptic delays introduced by the extra neurons in the pathway (see Figure 2.40b, Trace 2).

Trace 3, in Figure 2.40b, shows the response of a VBN cell to simultaneous stimulation of the centre and the outer area of its receptive field. In the figure, the inhibitory and excitatory responses have cancelled each other out. In reality, tactile stimuli are unlikely to balance out completely and there is likely to be at least a blip of activity at the onset of the tactile stimulus. This type of organization, involving antagonistic relationships between the outer and centre regions of concentrically organized receptive fields, forms the basis of an important general sensory processing device most often referred to as lateral inhibition but also called *surround inhibition* in some texts. You will encounter this fundamental neural mechanism for processing sensory information again in later blocks of this course.

Recordings from the somatosensory cortex reveal cells with a wide variety of quite different receptive field properties. The somatosensory cortex is not only the final destination of the afferent pathways, it is also an area where interactions are occurring which are the first stages in the analysis of the meaning of the sensory input. Next we will look at the structure of the cerebral cortex.

Summary of Section 2.3

The dorsal-column-medial-lemniscal (DCML) pathway is not the only specific pathway linking the tactile mechanoreceptors to the somatosensory cortex. Specific information is also conveyed via the spino-cervical-thalamic pathways, as well as being fed into non-specific pathways such as the spino-reticular tract.

There is considerable divergence within the DCML pathway which means that the output from one mechanoreceptor contributes to the incoming information for many cells that are further along the pathway that finally terminates in the somatosensory cortex. Equally, it is shown that, at every level, neurons have many convergent inputs. So the receptive fields of cells in the cortex, the thalamus (ventrobasal nucleus area), and the medulla (dorsal-column nuclei area) are defined by the number of mechanoreceptors that contribute to them. However, the receptive fields of these cells (in cortex, thalamus and medulla) have a central portion which when stimulated causes the cell to increase its firing rate above the non-stimulated background level of firing, and a surrounding area, which when stimulated causes the cell to decrease its firing rate below the background level. The reason that a stimulated area of skin can cause a cell to decrease its firing is because inhibitory interneurons have been activated within the part of the brain where these synaptic connections are being made (the medulla, the thalamus and the cortex). This is known as lateral (or surround) inhibition.

2.4 The cerebral cortex

2.4.1 Introduction

The cerebral cortex is the most distinctive feature of the human brain. Its convoluted surface dominates the dorsal surface of the brain (Figure 2.2). The convolutions arise because the sheet of layers of neurons forming the cortex has a much larger surface area than will easily fit into the relatively small skull. It is estimated that we have 10–15 thousand million neurons in this part of the brain and about ten times as many glial cells. Spread out, the cortex would have a surface area of 0.22 m², or the area of one page of a broadsheet newspaper. In fact, about two thirds of its surface area is buried in the valleys or **sulci** (singular, **sulcus**) that mark its surface in such a characteristic way. It varies in thickness from about 4 mm in the precentral **gyrus** (motor cortex) to 1.5 mm in the occipital cortex (the area primarily associated with vision). The pioneering English neurophysiologist, Charles Sherrington, described its intricate networks of neurons as 'an enchanted loom where millions of flashing shuttles weave a dissolving pattern'. A delightful description that captures some of the difficulties, and rewards, attached to the study of this area.

2.4.2 Anatomy of the cerebral cortex

A thin section through the human cortex has a characteristic appearance (Figure 2.42a).

Although it may not be immediately obvious from looking at Figure 2.42a, there are six anatomically distinguishable layers. These are six layers of cells identified by the sizes and shapes of their cell bodies. The overt horizontal pattern is due to variations

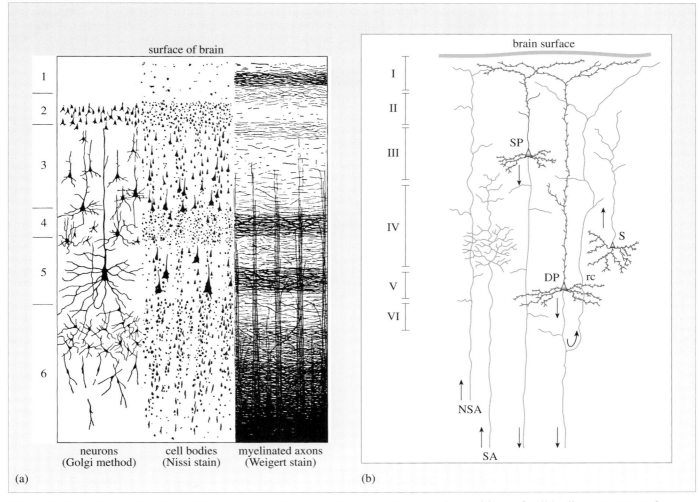

surface of brain

brain surface

neurons
(Golgi method)

cell bodies
(Nissi stain)

myelinated axons
(Weigert stain)

(a)

(b)

Figure 2.42   (a) A section through the human cortex variously stained to show the positions of cell bodies, neurons and axons. (b) Diagram showing the shape of some of the cells and the branching pattern of the axons from the thalamus and the association axons. Arrows show the direction of action potential travel. SA = specific afferents from the thalamus, NSA = non-specific afferents from the thalamus, SP = superficial pyramidal cell, DP = deep pyramidal cell, S = stellate cell, rc = recurrent collateral axon.

in the densities of cell bodies. By using a combination of different types of cell staining techniques, the nature of the cells in the different layers can be deduced (Figure 2.42a).

Each layer is conventionally referred to by a number, with the lowest number at the surface. (Some texts use Roman numerals, others use the Arabic system.) There is also a dominant vertical patterning, which is due to the grouping of neurons into *columns* running vertically down through the cortex. These columns are the basic functional units of the cortex, and you will find some information about their activity when you study each separate sense.

❍   In relation to touch, can you say from Figure 2.42b into which layer the dorsal column medial lemniscal (DCML) pathway will terminate?

●   The DCML pathway is the specific pathway that projects to the ventrobasal nucleus (VBN) of the thalamus and in Figure 2.42b you can see a bushy termination of a specific axon (SA) from the thalamus at level IV (4) of the cortex.

All specific pathways terminate at level IV (4) of the cortex and have extensive, compact terminal branches (often termed arborization). The non-specific afferents have different patterns of termination and show considerable variation in their degree of arborization.

The output from the cortex is provided by the **pyramidal cells**. There are two types of pyramidal cells, the *superficial* pyramidal cells found in layers II and III (2 and 3), and the larger, but less numerous, *deep* pyramidal cells in layers V and VI (5 and 6). Pyramidal cells have a particular arrangement of dendrites; they have a number of fairly short basal dendrites and a single, long apical dendrite which extends to layer I (1) where it has extensive branches. These can extend, laterally, along the cortex for up to 0.5 mm. The functional columns have a diameter of 0.3–1.0 mm and contain around 10,000 cell bodies so the pyramidal cells have the capability to integrate information from the thousands of cells within their column. The output from the deep pyramidal cells is to non-cortical parts of the brain. Their axons are often called **projection fibres**. Figure 2.42b shows these axons leaving the cortex via the ventral white matter beneath. The axons of the superficial pyramidal cells also descend through the cortex, leaving via the ventral white matter, but they go to other regions of the cortex rather than to other regions of the brain. You will find these axons that link different areas of cortex referred to as **association axons** (or fibres). Particularly long association axons are found in the structure that links the two cerebral hemispheres together, the **corpus callosum** (Figure 2.43). The axons of pyramidal cells also branch whilst still in the cortex. The branches are known as **collaterals**. Some of these collaterals are short *recurrent collaterals* which re-ascend through the cortex, branching at many points on their pathway (Figure 2.42b).

There are lots of other neurons of different sizes and shapes that exist entirely within the cortex. The axons of these interneurons, often called **intrinsic neurons,** communicate both vertically and horizontally but only within the cortex. The way in

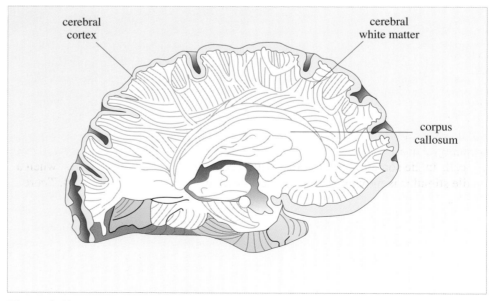

Figure 2.43 A sagittal section through the left cerebral hemisphere to show the fibre groups of the white matter and corpus callosum.

which the connections up and down and between the different layers are arranged suggests a columnar organization. The width of the columns is related to the lateral extent of the dendrites of the component cells. It was the American neurophysiologist, Vernon Mountcastle, who established that columns *were* the functional unit of the cortex.

So the column is a cylindrical volume of neurons that extends perpendicularly from the cortical surface. It contains neurons, their processes and inputs, which together act as a functional unit. Cortical processing occurs within these columns so that functionally each cortical region is a mosaic of columns rather than a sheet of neural tissue. Synaptic connections do occur between columns, and activity in one column may influence the activity in adjacent columns. But these lateral interactions act to change the intensity with which a column responds rather than changing the way it processes its incoming neuronal activity.

Mountcastle originally provided anatomical and neurophysiological evidence for the existence of columns in the somatosensory cortex almost half a century after Brodmann had identified 47 anatomically distinct regions of the cortex (see Block 1, Figure 5.4). The two observations are not contradictory. Whilst the columnar organization is typical of all areas of the cortex, the precise neuronal constituents do vary from region to region, giving rise to the cytoarchitectural variation described by Brodmann. The principles of neuronal processing remain the same regardless of whether the major input is from specific thalamic nuclei which will give the column a lot of densely packed axonal terminals in layer 4 or from non-specific nuclei which terminate diffusely throughout the cortex. There are also differences in the proportion of the other types of cells. For example, in the part of the cortex that receives the primary visual input, the **striate cortex**, there are a large number of tiny granule cells, far more than are found in other parts of the cortex. On the other hand pyramidal cells, found mostly in layers 3 and 5, are far fewer in number in the striate cortex than in other cortical regions. These differences presumably relate to the different kinds of processing that are undertaken in each of the areas.

As you might imagine, we can find out about the kinds of stimuli that excite cortical cells and gain details of their receptive field properties using single cell recording techniques as was done in the experiment shown in Figure 2.17. However, it is more problematic to record from a cortical neuron than a sensory neuron. Nevertheless, cells have been discovered that have quite complex receptive field properties, which tell us something about the way in which cortical processing starts to provide a meaningful analysis of the signals from the world 'out there'. As an example, there are cells in the somatosensory cortex with receptive fields that respond best when a tactile stimulus is moving in a particular direction, as shown in Figure 2.44. There will be more about cortical processing in subsequent blocks of this course.

Today we do not have to rely on single cell recordings. We now have very powerful tools that allow us to image the human brain whilst the owner of the brain remains conscious and (reasonably) comfortable and can follow instructions and report back on their perceptions. These functional imaging techniques are having a huge impact on current brain research and so we are devoting a longer section to describing them at the end of the block.

Figure 2.44   The responses of some neurons in the somatosensory cortex are directionally selective. Neurons 1 and 2 have receptive fields in the same position in the hand but have opposite directional preferences. (a) Neuron 1 responds when a stimulus is brushed towards the thumb, but neuron 2 does not respond. (b) Neuron 2 responds when the movement is in the other direction but now neuron 1 does not respond.

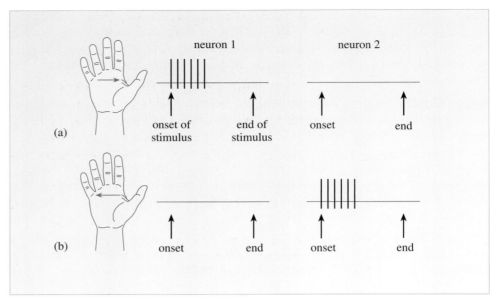

Summary of Section 2.4

The cerebral cortex has a layered appearance when viewed in cross-section which comprises six distinct layers. The thickness of the layers varies between different parts of the cortex according to their cellular make-up. All the specific input from the thalamus (i.e. from the DCML and SCT pathways) terminates in layer 4. Within the cortex, cells are grouped into columns and these columns are the functional units of the cortex where the incoming stimuli are processed. Their output is via the pyramidal cells.

Question 2.5

With respect to the system of touch and a neuron in the VBN of the thalamus, describe what is meant by the term 'receptive field'. Explain what is meant by saying it has antagonistic sub-regions. What type of processing gives rise to the property?

Question 2.6

Again with respect to the system of touch, compare and contrast the receptive field properties of neurons with cell bodies in the dorsal root ganglion (e.g. tactile mechanoreceptors) and those located in the VBN of the thalamus.

STUDY FILE

Activity 2.4

At this point you can read on or you can study the material 'Connections within the Brain' in the Overview section of *The Senses* multimedia program on the DVD. Note that it calls the fibres in the corpus callosum 'commissural fibres'. Commissural fibres are just association fibres that link the two hemispheres. Further instructions are given in the Block 2 *Study File*.

3

The neuron

From Section 2 we have gained an overview of the way in which neuronal systems
can cooperate in the processing of sensory information. Although we used touch as
our main example you should have been aware that we were illustrating principles
that have a wide general application. To appreciate some of the more detailed
analyses described in the Reader chapters it is necessary to know more about the
events taking place at the cellular level.

All cells are discrete entities bounded by membranes which have a similar function
to skin in that they keep the inside of the cell separate from the surrounding
extracellular fluid. But here the analogy ends because, to keep functioning, all cells
must take in new materials and expel unwanted metabolites. In addition, neurons
have to respond to signals and be capable of transmitting signals themselves. In
every instance the signal will originate from outside the cell and must somehow be
conveyed to the inside of the cell so that it can influence the molecular machinery of
the neuron. Control over what enters and leaves a cell resides with the membrane.
The membrane may be like a skin, but it is a skin in which doors can open and close.
Furthermore, new doors can appear and others disappear over timespans that can be
very short. So, understanding membrane structure and function holds the key to
understanding the functioning of neurons.

3.1 Neuronal membranes

The basic structure of the neuronal membrane (also called the plasma membrane) is
the same as other animal cell membranes.

○ From your study of previous courses, can you describe the basic structure of an
   animal cell membrane?

● The plasma membrane is made of a double layer of phospholipid molecules
   together with other lipids and also proteins (see Figure 3.1).

The membrane provides a barrier between the intracellular fluid, or cytoplasm, of
the cell and the extracellular fluid. It is responsible for protecting the finely balanced
machinery inside the cell from changes in the extracellular fluid. At the same time,
the cell's requirements for oxygen and glucose must be met and waste products must
be eliminated. So the membrane must selectively permit the entry and exodus of
appropriate molecules. The membrane's selectivity is fine-tuned to the cell's metabolic
needs, regulating the direction, amount and timing of the passage of molecules.

○ Look at Figure 3.1 and identify whereabouts molecules could pass through the
   membrane.

● One possibility is through channels formed by the integral proteins that span the
   membrane.

In Figure 3.1 the channels look fixed. In reality there are many different types of
membrane proteins and thus many different types of membrane channel and they
exhibit considerable fluidity in more than one respect. For example, there is a
dynamic turnover of membrane proteins and this is under genetic control. Proteins
are made by genes and you will find the term 'expressed' used in the Reader

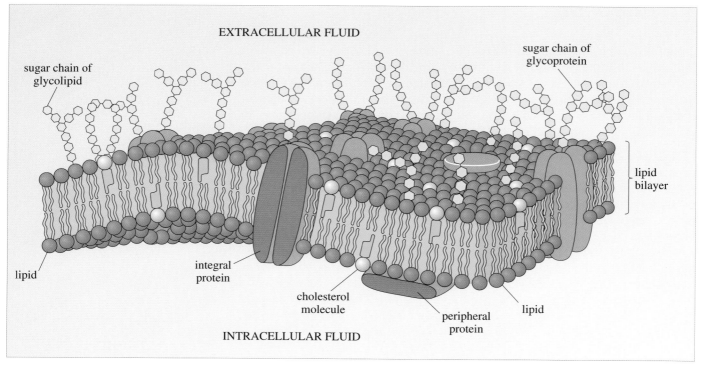

Figure 3.1   A schematic model showing the structure of a cell membrane. The long branched chains of sugars attached to proteins or lipids shown here are characteristic of the outer face of the cell membrane.

chapters to indicate that a gene is active. Thus, as gene activity fluctuates, some proteins go but are replaced by similar proteins, others may be removed but not replaced. New proteins may be inserted into the membrane or the density of existing proteins be altered.

In fact, the membrane as a whole is a fluid structure. Were this not so it would be impossible to make intracellular recordings using micropipettes (Box 2.2). When punctured by the needle-like point of the pipette, the membrane rapidly reseals. The phospholipid molecules simply flow around to fill the space, as water does around your body when you dive into a lake. All phospholipid molecules are able to move within their membrane layer, their tails rotating and flexing. However, some have more flexibility and therefore fluidity than others. This depends on the structure of the tail. One important variable is whether the fatty acid tail is made of chains that are saturated or unsaturated. The unsaturated fatty tails found in neuronal membranes are 'kinked' so they pack together more loosely and the membrane is therefore more fluid. Figure 3.2a shows the structure of **arachidonic acid**, a fatty acid component of a membrane lipid that is highly unsaturated and about which you will learn more in Block 5 because it is a precursor of the prostaglandins, which are chemicals involved in the detection of tissue damage.

The precise composition of the lipids in a membrane, their nature and the proportion of each type, varies from cell type to cell type, and also between different areas of the cell, in a consistent manner, so clearly there are limits to a lipid's fluidity of movement within the cell membrane. Figure 3.2b shows the chemical structure of sphingomyelin (which is abundant in the myelin sheath around the axons), Figure 3.2c shows a cerebroside (cerebrosides are glycolipids, that is lipids with sugar molecules

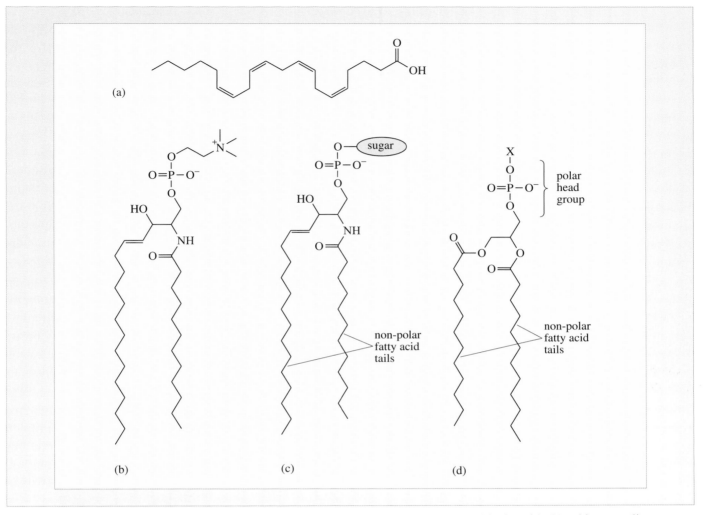

Figure 3.2   Simplified structure of some common neuronal membrane lipids: (a) arachidonic acid; (b) sphingomyelin, a sphingolipid; (c) a cerebroside glycolipid; (d) a glycerophospholipid.

attached to them, found in the membranes of some brain cells), and Figure 3.2d shows the general structure of a glycerophospholipid (common throughout the nervous system). These are shown for your interest and so that you don't think that membrane lipids are all little blue balls with yellow legs as depicted in Figure 3.1.

The two layers of the membrane are not symmetrically arranged. The inner and outer faces of the membrane differ in a distinctive way, as you can see in Figure 3.1.

○   Bearing in mind that signals from the outside have to cross the membrane to bring about changes within the cell, what structures are present on the outer face of the membrane (but not on the inner face) that might recognize and receive signalling molecules such as neurotransmitters?

●   Glycolipid and glycoprotein structures might fill this role.

These structures are called receptors. Many glycolipids are important in cell signalling and they are always found only on the outer surface of cell membranes.

This is also where glycoproteins (proteins with sugar molecules attached to them) are found, for the same reason.

In most cases, the neurotransmitters do not themselves cross the membrane but they provide the key to open the doors of our earlier analogy, that will allow the entry (or exit) of other molecules. But, even if the signalling molecule is lipid soluble and can itself cross the membrane, it usually binds (attaches) to some intracellular receptor, rather than having a direct effect on cellular metabolism. There will be examples of neurotransmitters that operate this way later in this section.

The properties of membranes are very greatly affected by their complement of proteins. Although the cell membrane can be as much as 50 per cent protein (by mass) you can see from Figure 3.1 that the proteins are, on average, much larger than the lipid molecules. They can be 50 times as large as a lipid molecule, and so in any cell membrane there are numerically fewer protein than lipid molecules.

The function of a protein molecule depends on its three-dimensional structure within the living membrane and this makes it difficult to study. However, some reasonable inferences can be made from the knowledge of protein functions.

Many of the signal-receiving molecules are proteins, the portion of the molecule that is exposed on the outer membrane surface being the receptor. The signalling molecule that binds to a receptor is known as a **ligand**. When a receptor-ligand complex is formed, and the membrane becomes porous to certain substances allowing them to pass through the cell membrane by *diffusion,* we assume that the protein has physically changed its shape. In other words, a conformational change has been brought about by the receptor-ligand complex resulting in the creation of a hole or pore in the membrane. In those few cases where evidence has been found for conformational changes in transmembrane proteins, the structure has been as theoretically predicted.

We are now in a position to look at the means by which substances can cross membranes.

3.2 Crossing the neuronal membrane

There are three main routes by which substances, both molecules and ions, cross membranes. They are: passive diffusion; transport by membrane proteins; and transport inside vesicles.

3.2.1 Passive diffusion

Some substances pass through the membrane without any specific interaction with the membrane's components, a process known as passive diffusion. These substances need to be fat soluble and fairly small. One example is ethanol (commonly known as alcohol). Alcohol rapidly crosses the stomach cells and is carried by the blood to other parts of the body to enter other cells within minutes of being imbibed. It used to be used as an anaesthetic during surgical procedures because it has the effect of depressing neuronal activity very rapidly. The more modern gaseous, inhalable anaesthetics enter brain cells having crossed the cell membranes from lung to bloodstream to brain equally rapidly, but they disrupt nerve function more than alcohol and the patient quickly becomes unconscious. Glue solvents also cross cell membranes by passive diffusion. All these substances can be regarded as neurotoxins because, with continued usage, they have the potential to damage neurons.

Passive diffusion also allows the small molecules of oxygen and carbon dioxide to enter and to leave cells respectively, moving down their concentration gradients from areas of high concentration to lower concentration. However, ions that are found in our bodies, such as sodium (Na^+) and calcium (Ca^{2+}), though small, have very limited permeability. One reason for this is that they are not fat soluble. Another reason is that in solution they have a shell of water molecules surrounding them and this makes them, for the practical purpose of wriggling through the lipid bilayer, too large. They can be moved across the membrane by the membrane proteins as we now explain.

3.2.2 Transmembrane transport by membrane proteins

There are two main types of transmembrane transport proteins. The simplest system is provided by the proteins forming **channels** through which specific substances can pass. There are a multitude of different protein channels and the mechanisms by which they come to be opened are various. The channels are also very specific in that each type only allows selected ions or molecules through. Once channels are open, transport across the membrane is very rapid, and does not require the cell to expend further energy. The molecules concerned cross the membrane by moving down their concentration gradient. This is known as facilitated diffusion. Figure 3.3a shows a model of facilitated diffusion through a protein channel. Glucose enters cells by facilitated diffusion.

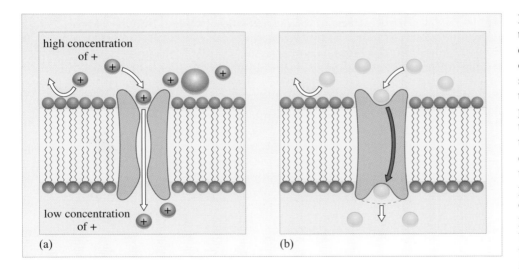

(a)

(b)

Figure 3.3   Models of membrane transport. (a) Protein channels: the curved arrow on the left hand side of the upper membrane surface shows an ion unable to pass through the lipid membrane. The purple ball represents an ion that is too large to traverse the membrane through this channel. In the centre of the diagram, ions pass through the protein channel. (b) Carrier proteins: the red arrow denotes a conformational change taking place that moves the binding site to the other side of the membrane taking its 'cargo' which is shown as a yellow ball.

Before leaving facilitated diffusion through channels, take a careful look at Figure 3.3a.

○   Is there any aspect of the model that looks unrealistic, that is, that looks as though it wouldn't work?

●   The top of the pore doesn't look wide enough to allow the red balls through.

Recent research suggests that some channels exercise specificity by binding to the substance to be transported before then releasing it into a channel through which it can diffuse.

The other kind of transmembrane transport protein is a **carrier** (also called **transporter**) and one model of this is shown in Figure 3.3b. Again, these provide passage through the membrane for very specific molecules or ions. A carrier has a binding site that recognizes and binds to a specific substance and, once bound, the protein alters its conformation in such a way that the binding site with its cargo is moved to the opposite side of the membrane, where a further change causes the release of the cargo. This is a much slower process than the facilitated diffusion through the protein channels. By the time one ion or molecule has been moved by this method at least 100 would have flowed through a channel. This is especially true when the carrier is taking its cargo from a low to a high concentration, that is transporting the cargo against its concentration gradient. Where the cargo is being transported against its concentration gradient the carrier is described as undertaking **active transport**. This requires energy which comes from the ubiquitous energy-providing molecule ATP (adenosine triphosphate). One example of active transport that is particularly important for the functioning of nerve cells is known as the **sodium pump**.

The sodium pump is also known as the **sodium-potassium pump** and the **sodium-potassium ATPase pump**, which gives you a pretty good idea of what is involved here. Essentially, it is an exchange mechanism for sodium (Na^+) and potassium (K^+) ions, powered by ATP.

There is a far greater concentration of Na^+ ions outside the cell than is found on the inside. The reverse is true for K^+ ions (see Table 3.1).

Table 3.1   Concentrations of ions inside and outside a human neuron.*

Ion [†]	Intracellular concentration/mmol l^{-1}	Extracellular concentration/mmol l^{-1}
Na^+	10	142
K^+	140	4
Ca^{2+}	10^{-4}	2.4
Mg^{2+}	58	1.2
Cl^-	4	103

* Only those few ions that have important roles in neuronal excitability are shown here so the positive and negative charges do not balance.

[†] In cells, most of the Na^+, K^+ and Cl^- ions are free in the cytoplasm and axoplasm but Mg^{2+} ions are mostly bound to proteins and most of the intracellular Ca^{2+} ions are concentrated inside organelles.

All cells have at least a fifteen-fold difference in concentration of these two ions across cellular membranes and to maintain normal cell activity it is essential to ensure that the differences are not eroded by ions diffusing down their concentration gradients, that is, Na^+ into the cell and K^+ out of the cell.

○   What mechanism prevents this occurring?

●   The cell membrane presents a barrier to both Na^+ and K^+ ions because they are not fat-soluble and, although they are small, they have shells of water molecules around them making them effectively larger entities (Section 3.2.1).

In fact, although Na$^+$ is the smaller ion, it has the larger shell around it, so K$^+$ ions are more able to occasionally slip through the membrane. In other words, the membrane is more permeable to K$^+$ ions. Nevertheless, there is some leakage of both Na$^+$ and K$^+$ through the cell membrane. This is corrected and the cell's internal concentrations of both ions maintained by the action of the sodium pump (see Figure 3.4).

You will notice that this energy-consuming process results in more Na$^+$ ions leaving the cell than K$^+$ ions entering.

○   Is this what you would expect to be necessary in order to maintain the status quo?

●   No! The membrane is more permeable to K$^+$ ions so you would expect there to be more K$^+$ ions needing to be returned to the cell's interior than Na$^+$ ions needing to be removed.

An explanation here is that Na$^+$ ions are carried into cells in other ways. One example is a secondary active transport system which is linked to the removal of hydrogen (H$^+$) ions (see Figure 3.5 overleaf). The energy provided by Na$^+$ ions is allowed to flow into the cell down their concentration gradient. H$^+$ ions are produced as a consequence of acid-forming reactions of cell metabolism and it is important to get rid of them as the cell's pH must be rigorously regulated to keep it at the metabolic optimum of about 7.2.

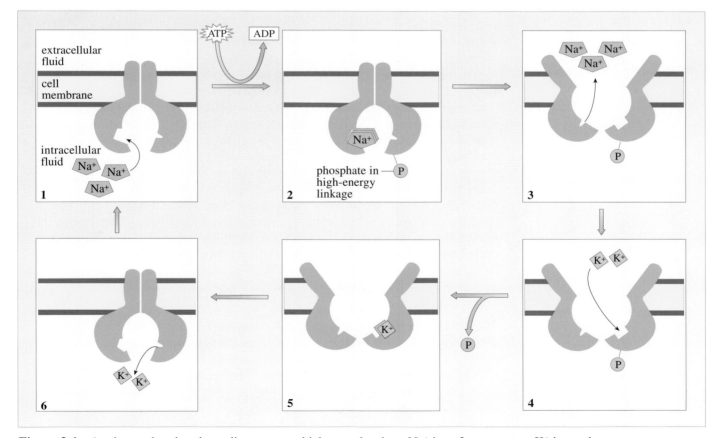

Figure 3.4   A scheme showing the sodium pump which extrudes three Na$^+$ ions for every two K$^+$ ions taken up.

Figure 3.5 Schematic representation of the primary active transport of Na^+ and K^+ ions by the sodium pump and the secondary active transport of Na^+ and H^+ ions.

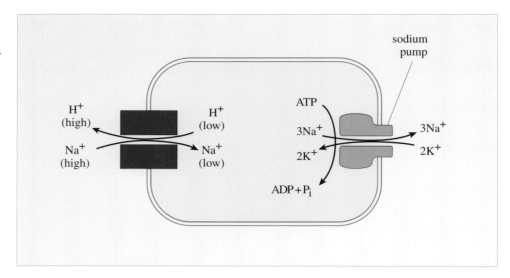

In describing these two processes, namely the active transport provided by the sodium pump (a 'carrier' protein) and a simple pore for positive ions to diffuse through (a 'channel' protein) we have only looked at the two extremes of a continuum of transport mechanisms across cell membranes that are provided by the membrane proteins. We now turn to the third route available to substances traversing the membrane: transport inside membrane-derived vesicles.

3.2.3 Trans-membrane transport inside membrane-derived vesicles

There are some molecules that are simply too big to be transported across membranes using any kind of pore. But there is an ingenious method that allows large molecules to be moved across membranes, in either direction, by first wrapping them in a membrane. When exporting substances that the cell has manufactured, such as neurotransmitters, the packaging of the neurotransmitter into a membrane-coated vesicle is organized by an organelle called the **Golgi apparatus** (or **Golgi complex**). When the neuron is stimulated to release the neurotransmitter, the membrane of the vesicle fuses with the cell membrane and releases the neurotransmitter into the gap between itself and the target cell. Where the target cell is also a neuron, the gap is called the **synaptic cleft**. Material is taken into a cell by a similar process but it is the cell membrane itself that wraps around, or engulfs, the items to be brought into the cell. It does this by forming extensions or pseudopods (false feet) around the material, which coalesce once they have totally surrounded the item. This structure can then pinch off as an internal vesicle. Importing material by this means is known as **endocytosis**, and exporting material is known as **exocytosis** (see Figure 3.6).

These particular events need to be viewed against the background of continuing cellular metabolism that recycles the cell constituents throughout life. So although neurons are cells that do not replicate and must last for the body's lifetime, they are not like manufactured commodities which, once created, are static for all time. There is a constant turnover of cell constituents, different items turning over at different rates and many of these rates being able to fluctuate on demand. By the mechanisms of exo- and endocytosis the cell membrane can be constantly renewed and the balance of its constituents altered. For example, if a great deal of neurotransmitter were being released by one neuron it would be possible to damp

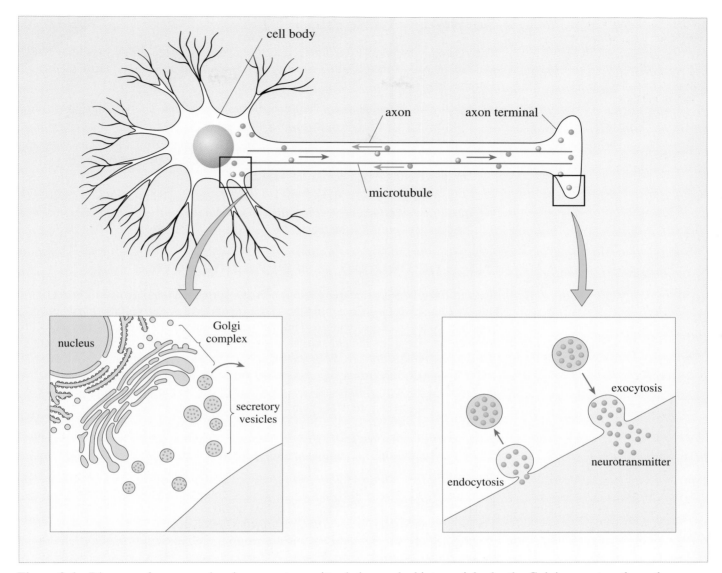

Figure 3.6 Diagram of a neuron showing neurotransmitter being packed into vesicles by the Golgi apparatus, the pathway being taken by the vesicles to the axon terminal, and the processes of endocytosis and exocytosis.

down its effect on the target cell by using endocytosis to withdraw proteins with receptors for the neurotransmitters from the target cell's membrane. This is known as down regulation of a receptor. There are other methods of down regulation which can also effectively reduce the numbers of receptors available to a particular neurotransmitter. Down regulation could be responsible for some instances of abnormal mood changes and perceptual experiences and is also one of the factors underlying the cellular response to the drug heroin, and explains its decreasing effectiveness with continued usage. There will be more about this in Block 5.

Now that we know that the cell membrane is so complex and that its structure varies over space and time, we are in a good position to understand how the neuron can be such a good signalling device.

Summary of Section 3.2

The neuronal membrane provides a selective barrier between the extracellular fluid and the interior of the cell. There are three ways that substances can cross the membrane:

- by passive diffusion down their concentration gradient. This mechanism only operates for small, fat-soluble molecules;
- with the assistance of membrane proteins. These range from those that open up channels through which a substrate can then diffuse to those that bind to the substance and carry it across the membrane;
- in membrane-bound vesicles. The substance is packaged into a vesicle, the membrane of which coalesces with the cell membrane thereby allowing the substance to cross the membrane.

3.3 The neuron as a signalling device

Each of the millions of neurons in our nervous system can, at any one moment, receive thousands of different inputs. These inputs give rise to cellular changes, which are integrated and which affect the output from that neuron. For neurons with long axons 'output' is the generation of an action potential. By this we mean that synaptic potentials, which can be excitatory or inhibitory, are integrated, and then action potentials (electrical signals) are generated in axons. The arrival of action potentials at the axonal terminals (of which there can be thousands) precipitates the release of neurotransmitters at chemical synapses or further electrical activity at electrical synapses. These signals then influence the next element in the pathway. Other types of cells can, and do, respond to and secrete signalling molecules. Only neurons have a means of communicating incredibly rapidly over long distance by generating action potentials.

3.3.1 The action potential

The ability of neurons to generate and transmit action potentials depends on two features. Firstly, the chemical contents of neurons are different from the fluids on the outside of the membrane (Figures 2.5 and 3.7, and Table 3.1) and secondly, the membrane can change its permeability to some of these chemicals in an organized way.

○ How does the concentration of Na^+ inside the neuron differ from that outside the cell?

● The concentration of Na^+ inside the neuron is lower than that in the extracellular fluid (Table 3.1).

○ How does the composition of K^+ inside the neuron differ from that outside the cell?

● The situation is the reverse. K^+ is at a higher concentration inside the neuron.

This feature is not unique to neurons, it is true for all the cells in your body. The feature that is unique to neurons (and some types of muscles) is the way that the axonal membrane can change the nature of the barrier it presents to these two ions.

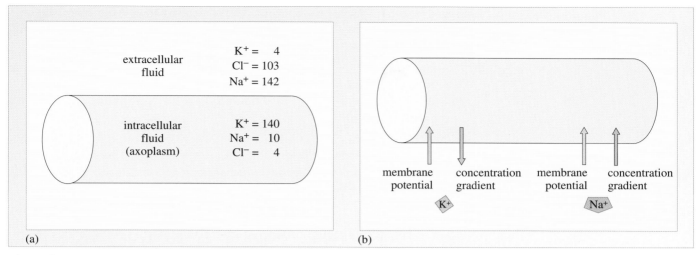

Figure 3.7   (a) Concentration of the major ions on the inside and outside of an axon. The units are millimoles/kg of fluid. Note that in addition to these ions, some others (e.g. magnesium and calcium and large organic molecules) will also be present. (b) Factors affecting the movements of ions across the axonal membrane.

In a precise and controlled way it allows, sequentially, rapid movement of these ions across the membrane. As these charged ions dart across a patch of membrane we can record the changes in electrical activity. It is these changes that are described as the action potential.

○   How do you suppose these ions cross the membrane?

●   Through the opening of protein channels in the axonal membrane. This you will remember is the most rapid mechanism for crossing the membrane (Section 3.2.2).

The channels that are of particular importance are ones that are opened, not by a ligand but by a change in voltage. They are therefore called **voltage-gated ion channels** (also *voltage-dependent channels*).

When the axon is not transmitting an action potential it is described as being in a resting state. This does not mean that nothing is happening, rather, the activity is in a dynamic steady state. There are unequal concentrations of ions on either side of the membrane, the membrane does not totally prevent movement of ions and there is a sodium pump working away. So there is movement of ions through the membrane in both directions but no *net* change, that is, there is a dynamic equilibrium.

Recording from a resting membrane shows that there is a potential gradient across the membrane and the inside of the cell is negative with respect to the outside. This is known as the **resting membrane potential**.

When considering what is happening to the classic neuron (Figure 2.6), the usual value given for the resting membrane potential is that the inside of the neuron is −70 mV (millivolts) when compared to the extracellular fluid. However, there is variation because the dynamic state depends on just how permeable a particular membrane is for the charged ions and on the density of pumps and other ion channels that can be transiently open. Consequently, not all neurons exhibit the same potential difference across their membrane.

○ If one considers the Na⁺ ion in isolation, the negative membrane potential and the sodium concentration gradient will each exert a force that will tend to move the ion across the membrane. In which direction will each work?

● The concentration of Na⁺ is higher outside the cell so the concentration gradient will tend to pull Na⁺ into the cell. Na⁺ is a positive ion so it will be drawn toward the more negative area. So both forces are acting to pull Na⁺ into the cell.

○ What is the situation for the K⁺ ion?

● As K⁺ is a positive ion the potential gradient across the membrane will tend to pull K⁺ ions into the cell. But the concentration gradient for K⁺ is in the opposite direction tending to draw K⁺ ions out of the cell. In fact, overall, the tendency is for K⁺ to be expelled.

○ In the resting neuron, what other force is at work?

● The sodium pump is working to maintain the concentration gradient of K⁺ and Na⁺ ions across the membrane.

For every two K⁺ ions that the sodium pump carries into the cell it expels three Na⁺ ions.

However, if there were to be any change in the membrane potential, or if the permeability of the membrane were to change, for example, should extra channels open, then this would lead to a change in the individual movement, and hence the net movement of ions. The basis for the generation of action potentials is that the membrane does alter its permeability for very short time periods and that these transient and selective changes in permeability are only triggered when the resting membrane potential becomes less negative, i.e. it **depolarizes**. The amount of depolarization needed to trigger the opening of voltage-gated sodium channels is about 7 mV. In other words, the resting membrane potential becomes less negative.

○ If the resting membrane potential is −70 mV what is the potential when there is a depolarization of 5 mV?

● The membrane potential would be −65 mV.

The membrane potential is now less negative but depolarization is insufficient to trigger an action potential. However, when the potential moves to −63 mV, a depolarization of 7 mV, the voltage-gated sodium channels open, allowing the movement of Na⁺ ions across the membrane, that is, the start of the action potential.

○ What is the name given to the membrane potential that triggers opening of the voltage-gated sodium channels?

● This is the threshold level (Section 2.1.1).

○ In which direction will the Na⁺ ions move, and why?

● Na⁺ ions move into the cell, down their concentration and potential gradients.

○ With the influx of Na⁺ ions what will happen to the membrane potential?

● The membrane potential decreases, as the inside of the cell becomes less negative then positive.

The number of Na⁺ ions that flow rapidly into the neuron is very small in terms of overall numbers, and makes no appreciable impact on the relative concentration values. However, each ion carries through a small positive charge and, with no additional negative charges to counterbalance them, there is a large change in the membrane potential (Figure 3.8). The inside of the membrane becomes more positive than the outside, the potential moving from -70 mV to $+30$ mV (or thereabouts). The magnitude of the positive charge inside the neuron does not increase further because potassium voltage-gated channels open very shortly after the sodium voltage-gated channels do, and so positive charge, in the form of K⁺ ions, leaves the cell; the force of the concentration gradient for K⁺ being greater than the (rapidly diminishing) negative membrane potential. Indeed the membrane potential may already be positive by the time K⁺ ions are able to leave the cell, so they would be moving down both an electrical and a chemical gradient. The membrane now rapidly returns to its resting potential, that is it **repolarizes**. In part this is brought about by the efflux of K⁺ ions but the other relevant event is that the sodium voltage-gated channels close.

Figure 3.8b shows the pattern traced out by the changing potential values that are picked up by a recording microelectrode and gives a description of the events underlying the visual changes as the *spike* is generated. You will notice that after the spike has passed, the recorded value from the electrode reaches resting potential and then dips even lower. In other words, the inside of the cell becomes more negative than it is when it is in the resting state. This phase is termed **hyperpolarization** and it happens because the potassium voltage-gated channels are still open and K⁺ is still leaving the cell in response to its concentration gradient. Resting potential is regained once the K⁺ channels close. The period of time when the cell is hyperpolarized is called the **refractory period**. It is sub-divided into an initial **absolute refractory period**, when no action potential can be generated because the sodium voltage-gated

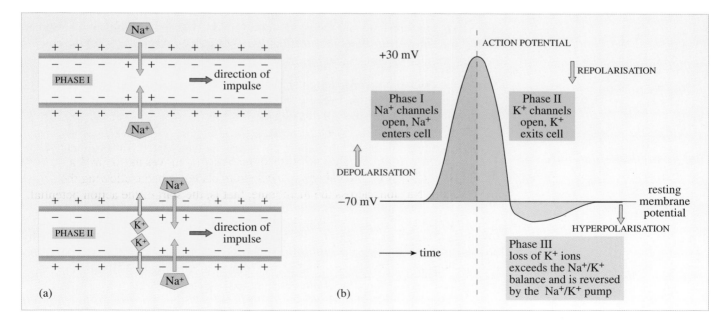

Figure 3.8   (a) Ion movement and (b) Changes in membrane potential during generation of an action potential. Phase I: opening of voltage-gated Na⁺ channels allows the entry of Na⁺ into the cell, causing depolarization. Phase II: opening of voltage-gated K⁺ channels allows exit of K⁺ ions from the cell, bringing the membrane potential down once more. Phase III: loss of K⁺ ions exceeds the Na⁺/ K⁺ balance and is reversed by the Na⁺/ K⁺ pump. Closing of voltage-gated Na⁺ channels prevents further Na⁺ entry into the cell.

channels simply will not open regardless of how much depolarizing stimulus they receive, and a **relative refractory period** when they will open but only on receipt of a larger than usual depolarizing stimulus that takes the membrane to the threshold value. The refractory period lasts between 0.5 and 1 ms, depending on the nature of the axon, and it places an upper limit on the frequency of action potentials. You already know (Section 2.1.1) that this is about 1000 Hz (i.e. no more than 1000 action potentials per second).

○ Whereabouts is the action potential generated?

● At the axon hillock (Section 2.1.1).

It is at the axon hillock that incoming signals first encounter an area of neuronal membrane that has these specialized voltage-gated ion channels. Other parts of the neuronal membrane are not able to respond to incoming depolarizing stimuli by generating action potentials because they do not possess these specialized membrane proteins. When signals are received from other neurons, or from sensory receptors, the signalling molecules bind to receptor sites that open or close ion channels (as described in the previous section), and ions can enter or leave the neuron, resulting in depolarizing or hyperpolarizing signals spreading from these synaptic input sites (more details later in this section). But it is only if the sum total of all these different inputs reaches the depolarizing threshold value *at the axon hillock* that an action potential is generated.

The action potential is then transmitted along the axon from this source because there is a passive sideways spread of the Na^+ ions along the undersurface of the cell membrane. The charge they carry depolarizes these adjacent areas of membrane so that *their* voltage-gated Na^+ channels open, triggering another wave of electrical activity at a small distance from the source. In this way adjacent areas of axon are depolarized to threshold and the signal transmitted to the axon terminals. The spread of Na^+ ions is, of course, in all directions away from the axon hillock but the cell body membrane cannot respond because it has no voltage-gated Na^+ channels.

The action potential travels along the axon to the axon terminals. The movement is never in the other direction because the spread of Na^+ ions to the area of membrane that has just fired is functionally valueless.

○ Why should this be so when these areas have voltage-gated Na^+ channels?

● These areas have recently responded and will still be in the refractory phase.

We talk and write of action potentials travelling or being transmitted but in reality the individual action potential is generated, and decays within a small area of membrane, and in so doing, it causes another action potential to be generated nearby and so on. A much used analogy is that of a firecracker fuse. Once the first point of the fuse has been lit it brings the adjacent segment of the fuse to its ignition temperature and this process continues right to the end of the fuse.

The speed of this electrical signalling along the axon can be very fast indeed. Different neurons conduct at different speeds and the speed is termed the **conduction velocity**.

○ What factors influence the speed of conduction?

● The diameter of axon is one important feature (Table 2.2).

The reason for this is that the extent to which the sideways spread of Na$^+$ ions (from the portion of membrane where an action potential is being generated) is attenuated depends on the diameter of the axon. In a small diameter axon you have to be able to generate the next action potential fairly close to the original one because at greater distances there will not have been a sufficient flow of charge to depolarize the membrane. Axons are not uniformly supplied with voltage-gated ion channels along their length, and small diameter axons will need to have patches where action potentials can be generated at more frequent intervals than large diameter axons.

Another factor that affects speed of conduction is the myelin sheath. You will recall that during development of the glial cell that gives rise to the myelin sheath, all glial cytoplasm was squeezed out of the layers that wrapped around the neuron axon (Figure 2.12). In myelinated portions of the axon there is no ion-containing extracellular fluid in the area around the outer face of the axonal membrane, but several layers of fatty glial membranes which act as excellent electrical insulation. No current can flow through these portions of axonal membrane. (They are also almost devoid of appropriate channels so that if they become demyelinated they *cannot* generate action potentials. This is the critical factor underlying the functional deficits observed in demyelinating diseases such as multiple sclerosis.) When an action potential is generated in a myelinated axon the sideways spread of Na$^+$ ions is less attenuated than you might expect, because there is no leakage through the axonal membrane lying beneath layers of the fatty glial membrane. Sufficient depolarization to bring a responding membrane to threshold can be detected 1–2 mm away from the source. In myelinated axons, breaks in the myelin occur at the appropriate distances (1–2 mm, the exact value depending on other properties of the axon such as its diameter). At these breaks, called nodes of Ranvier (Section 2.1.1), there are high densities of the voltage-gated ion channels, and so the generation of action potentials jumps from node to node. Not only is this *saltatory* (leaping) conduction far faster than the spread of action potentials down unmyelinated axons, it also involves the manufacture of fewer ion channels (ion channels are proteins that the cell has to manufacture at a metabolic cost), and the manufacture and operation of fewer sodium pumps. So, overall this is a most efficient system.

Once the electrical activity reaches the axon terminals, the next stage in the transfer of information between neurons involves a synapse; electrical or chemical.

Activity 3.1

At this point take a break from reading to work through the Nerve Cell section of *The Senses* multimedia program on the DVD. Further instructions are given in the Block 2 *Study File*.

3.3.2 The synapse

The synapse is the point of interaction between two cells and has components that belong to each cell.

All possible combinations of one part of a neuron synapsing with any part of another occur. They are each given descriptive names that tell you the anatomy of the synapse. For example, an *axo-dendritic* synapse is one where the axon of one neuron synapses onto the dendrite of another. An *axo-axonal* synapse has the axon of one neuron making an input onto the axon of another (Figure 3.9 overleaf).

Figure 3.9 (a) An axo-dendritic synapse; (b) an axo-axonal synapse.

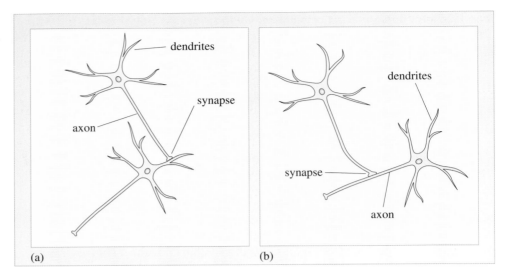

(a)   (b)

The expression presynaptic cell (presynaptic unit or presynaptic neuron are alternative terms) and postsynaptic cell are commonly used. Activity in the presynaptic unit influences the postsynaptic unit. Information is passed from the presynaptic to the postsynaptic unit and, as was briefly mentioned in Section 2.1.1, the mechanism of transfer can be electrical (an electrical synapse, Figure 2.9b) or by means of the passage of molecules of neurotransmitter (a chemical synapse, Figure 2.9a). For various reasons, mostly relating to the limitations of available technology, we currently have less information on electrical synapses but this does not mean that they are of any less importance in the processing of information within the CNS.

Electrical synapses

As just mentioned, there is rather little known about these synapses. They occur where two cells have their membranes making such close contact that there are cell to cell pores through which ions can pass. In effect, electrical activity, which may be the action potential propagation, proceeds from one cell to the next unimpeded. So one striking feature of an electrical synapse is that there is no **synaptic delay**. Another feature is that, theoretically, impulses can pass in either direction. You might think this information to be irrelevant because the way that neurons are joined up with each other to make pathways would allow only one direction of signal transfer. But you have seen (Figure 3.9) that any part of a neuron can make contact with any part of another neuron and that cells packed together in cortical columns (Section 2.3.1, and Figure 2.42) will be networking rather than passing information in a sequential pathway. So a cell with an electrical synapse can be pre- or postsynaptic at different times. Some electrical synapses have a preferred direction of operation, they are said to be *rectified*, but all are capable of bidirectional operation. The extent of electrical synaptic connections to be found within the brain is uncertain, but it seems that in many instances cell to cell electrical contact can be modulated by chemical signalling. For instance, in the retina there are many electrical synapses between cells, known as *horizontal cells*. The effectiveness of these synaptic connections are decreased by a neurotransmitter called dopamine and this alters the horizontal cells' receptive fields. There will be more about this in Block 4.

Chemical synapses

Information travels in one direction only across the chemical synapse, so the chemical synapses are all rectified.

Electrical activity, such as the arrival of an action potential causes a neurotransmitter to be released from the terminal of the presynaptic neuron. Neurotransmitters are both synthesized and stored within neurons. By diffusion, the neurotransmitter crosses the gap (known as the *synaptic cleft*) between the two cells. It then influences the postsynaptic cell. As you have already learned, there is a synaptic delay at a chemical synapse. The diffusion of the neurotransmitter across the synaptic cleft is relatively slow when compared to the speed at which information is transmitted across an electrical synapse.

○ How great is the synaptic delay?

● There is a delay of about 1 ms between the arrival of the action potential at the presynaptic terminal and any electrical change in the postsynaptic cell (Section 2.1.1).

○ How might a neurotransmitter alter membrane permeability?

● The receptor-ligand complex might open a channel or activate a carrier (Section 3.2.2) allowing specific ions to enter or leave the postsynaptic cell.

In a moment we will see that this is not the only mechanism whereby neurotransmitters alter membrane permeability, but in all cases the consequence will be either depolarization or hyperpolarization of the postsynaptic neuron. Which of these two effects occurs at any given synapse depends upon the nature of the transmitter and the type of receptor found in the postsynaptic membrane. So a transmitter that binds with a type A receptor at one synapse and opens a channel that was specific to, say, K^+ ions will cause hyperpolarization. Yet the same transmitter at a different synapse having no type A receptors, could bind to a type B receptor that opens a channel for, say, Na^+ ions and this will cause depolarization. If the transmitter causes depolarization of the postsynaptic unit, it is said to be an excitatory synapse. Conversely, if hyperpolarization results, the synapse is said to be inhibitory. On the basis of the change in potential that occurs following the arrival of the transmitter, we refer to **excitatory postsynaptic potentials (EPSP)** and **inhibitory postsynaptic potentials (IPSP)**. Note that we do not refer to an excitatory (or inhibitory) transmitter, although we can often characterize a neurotransmitter as having an excitatory (or inhibitory) effect in most synaptic situations. Note also that Na^+ and K^+ ions are not the only ions to affect membrane potential. The movement of any ion type across the cell membrane will alter membrane potential.

The synaptic delay of around 1 ms was earlier attributed to the fact that the neurotransmitter has to diffuse across the synaptic cleft. But the time taken for a neurotransmitter to diffuse across the synaptic cleft is actually less than 0.5 ms, so there must be other events taking place at the chemical synapse which consume some of the time associated with synaptic delay. In the first instance you might be wondering how the arrival of an action potential at the presynaptic membrane triggers the release of the neurotransmitter.

○ How is the neurotransmitter stored at the presynaptic membrane?

● It is packaged into membrane-coated vesicles (Section 3.2).

These vesicles fuse with the cell membrane and release the neurotransmitter molecules into the synaptic cleft.

What triggers this process? The first event to occur after the depolarization of the presynaptic membrane due to the arrival of an action potential is a rapid influx of Ca^{2+} ions. This can be detected as a local increase in calcium ion concentration as well as contributing to a local change in membrane potential.

○ Can you suggest a mechanism whereby the depolarizing stimulus of the action potential could cause Ca^{2+} ions to enter the neuron in the region of the presynaptic membrane?

● You might suspect (and rightly so) that there were voltage-gated calcium channels in that portion of the cell membrane.

So the depolarization occasioned by the arrival of the action potential causes voltage-gated calcium channels to open. Calcium ions enter the cell driven by both their concentration gradient (Table 3.1 and Figure 3.7) and the potential gradient. The increased concentration of Ca^{2+} ions at the presynaptic membrane causes conformational changes to occur in proteins that are involved in holding the synaptic vesicles in position. These *docking proteins*, acting with other proteins, are then able to bring about the fusion of the vesicle membrane with the cell membrane, allowing the neurotransmitter to spill out into the synaptic cleft (Figure 3.10).

Figure 3.10   Diagram of a chemical synapse.

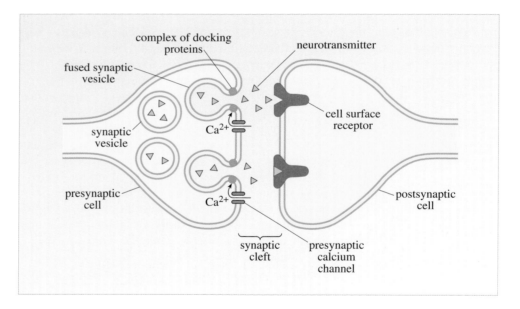

○ What name do we give to this mechanism of releasing neurotransmitters from vesicles?

● This is an example of exocytosis (Section 3.2.3).

We have been talking about the arrival of an action potential causing release of the neurotransmitter but in Section 2 brief mention was made of neurons that communicate using neurotransmitter release yet do not generate action potentials. These neurons are probably the more numerous type in the brain.

○   How can neurons that do not generate action potentials release neurotransmitters?

●   It was stated that the axonal membrane potential of these cells altered in response to the summated effects of the synaptic inputs to the cell. The account given above indicates that it is the *depolarization* of the membrane that causes the voltage-gated calcium channels to open. Thus these neurons will release neurotransmitters from their presynaptic membranes whenever the depolarization is sufficient to activate the opening of the voltage-gated calcium channels.

No sooner is the neurotransmitter released into the synaptic cleft than it starts to be removed. This may be by enzymatic breakdown of the neurotransmitter molecules, the breakdown products then being taken back into the presynaptic cell, or the whole neurotransmitter molecule may be recycled, being taken back into the presynaptic cell by endocytosis. This latter re-uptake mechanism allows the same molecules to be re-used many times, obviously an advantage in saving metabolic energy. In some cases neurotransmitter molecules diffuse out of the synaptic cleft and glial cells capture them by endocytosis. If there were no active mechanisms removing neurotransmitter molecules from the synaptic cleft, the neurotransmitter would influence the postsynaptic cell for a prolonged period, until it eventually diffused out of the synaptic cleft. Active removal (or breakdown) of the neurotransmitter ensures that the postsynaptic cell receives a sharp signal which is in proportion to the electrical stimulus that triggered it, rather than a long and diffuse signal. Obviously there can be sustained postsynaptic activity if there is sustained activity in the presynaptic cell. Sustained depolarization leads to a greater release of neurotransmitter and a train of action potentials produces a greater release of neurotransmitter than a single action potential. The frequency of action potentials determines the size and duration of the chemical stimulus that is transmitted.

Those molecules of neurotransmitters that cross the synaptic cleft usually bind to receptors on the postsynaptic membrane, which are of two kinds. They are either **ionotropic receptors**, the ligand-gated receptors that open or close pores through the membrane, thus regulating the passage of a specific ion (Section 3.2.2), or **metabotropic receptors** that produce an intracellular effect. In the latter case the neurotransmitter binds to a protein receptor site and this causes a change to the part of the protein that is inside the cell. Although this does not immediately alter the membrane permeability, ultimately the effect is the same and a specific ion channel will open or close through the activity of intermediary molecules, often known as **second messengers**. Many of the membrane proteins which operate by this indirect mechanism are bound to guanosine diphosphate (GDP) and are known as **G-protein receptors**. These play a major role in the senses of smell and taste (Block 6). Typically, the protein molecule is folded in such a way that it crosses the membrane seven times (Figure 3.11). One advantage of this indirect method of altering membrane permeability is that there is the possibility of greatly magnifying (or amplifying) the response (Figure 3.12).

Finally, there are a few neurotransmitters that do not bind to the postsynaptic membrane but pass through the cell membrane and initiate a cellular response themselves.

○   What kinds of molecules would be able to do this?

●   They must be fat soluble and fairly small (Section 3.2.1).

Both nitric oxide (NO) and carbon monoxide (CO) have recently been found to have this type of neurotransmitter function, in that they pass between neurons and alter

Figure 3.11 A G-protein receptor is activated by a neurotransmitter and acts to open an ion channel. (a) The ion channel is closed. (b) The ion channel is still closed but the neurotransmitter has bound to the G-protein receptor causing it to interact with and activate the G-protein. (c) The activated G-protein has opened the ion channel.

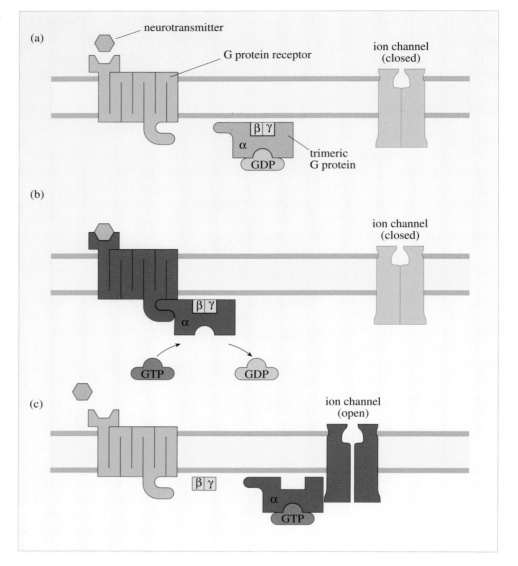

Figure 3.12 (a) A neurotransmitter is about to bind to a metabotropic receptor. (b) The activated receptor sends signals to second messengers. In turn, the second messengers pass on and amplify the signal.

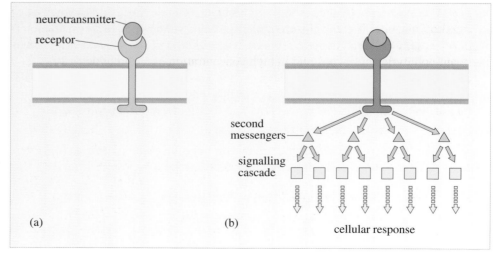

membrane permeability in the postsynaptic neuron. They are both gases and are not stored in synaptic vesicles so their mode of release is different from that just described. However their mode of action is to effect the production of cyclic guanosine mono-phosphate (cGMP) which acts as a second messenger. They are both inactivated very rapidly (within 5–10 seconds half of the NO molecules will have been inactivated) so they do not spread far from their source but they can from one source affect several cells (including glia) because they are not dependent upon there being specific receptors to enable them to influence another cell.

It should now be clear that, depending upon the type of neuron involved, there are different processes involving the release of the neurotransmitter, its diffusion across the synaptic cleft and its interaction with the postsynaptic membrane and that these processes can account for some of the time associated with the synaptic delay. Whatever the precise mechanisms involved, a chemical synapse, when activated, has the effect of having either a depolarizing or hyperpolarizing effect on the postsynaptic cell.

The postsynaptic cell will receive many synaptic inputs and we now consider how these are integrated in cells where the response can only be to fire or not to fire the all-or-nothing action potential.

Box 3.2   Neurotransmitters

Different neurotransmitters diffuse at different rates. There are at least 60 different neurotransmitter molecules, and probably many more substances exist that are likely to function as neurotransmitters in different parts of the brain. Table 3.2 (overleaf) gives the names of some neurotransmitters and the places where they are to be found. Our understanding of synapses is based on detailed studies of a few neurotransmitters only, but these seem to function in the same manner. In general, the released transmitter interacts with membrane receptors of the postsynaptic unit, changing membrane permeability and hence membrane potential.

It is not always easy to be certain that a substance is a neurotransmitter because, for example, the amino acid neurotransmitters glutamate, glycine and GABA (γ-aminobutyric acid) are found in high concentrations in all cells.

In the brain, GABA and glycine usually activate inhibitory synapses so they are often called inhibitory neurotransmitters. Glutamate is, for the same reason, often called an excitatory neurotransmitter.

In general, each neurotransmitter has more than one receptor type it can activate. Glutamate activates at least four receptor types, of which three are ionotropic (ion-gated). One of these ionotropic receptors is the NMDA receptor, so called because N-methyl-D-

aspartic acid (NMDA) is particularly effective at activating it. Receptors are not necessarily exclusive to a neurotransmitter. For example, in Block 6 in the section on taste, you will come across NMDA receptors that are activated by external stimuli, namely chemicals that we can taste.

Although only one glutamate receptor is metabotropic (i.e. activates a secondary reaction to open gates), in general this indirect, metabotropic linkage between a neurotransmitter and the channel it opens is a more common situation than ionotropic, ligand-receptor binding. However, in many cases where the neurotransmitter does not open a gate directly, but acts via second messenger G proteins often enhancing the response to another neurotransmitter, it would be more correct to speak of it as a neuromodulator. Peptides such as enkephalins, endorphins, substance P, dynorphin and cholecystokinin are neuromodulators.

Despite the difficulties in determining whether a substance is a neurotransmitter, a neuromodulator, or involved in some other metabolic activity, once it has been established that a neuron uses a particular neurotransmitter (e.g. GABA, adrenalin) it is named accordingly (GABAergic, adrenergic). The responding receptors would be known as GABAergic or adrenergic receptors.

Table 3.2   The names and sources of some neurotransmitters.

Neurotransmitter Group	Neurotransmitter	Location
acetylcholine	acetylcholine (Ach)	CNS/ANS*/neuromuscular junction
catecholamines	dopamine noradrenalin/norepinephrin adrenalin/epinephrin	CNS/sensory and motor pathways brain/ANS brain/ANS
indoleamines	serotonin (5HT)	CNS/ANS
amino acids	GABA (γ-amino-butyric acid) glutamate aspartate glycine histamine	brain brain brain CNS brain
neuropeptides	endorphins enkephalins dynorphins substance P somatostatin galanin cholecystokinin (CCK) bradykinin	brain/ANS brain/ANS brain brain/ANS/nociceptor brain/ANS brain/ANS brain/ANS brain/ANS

* CNS = central nervous system, ANS = autonomic nervous system.

3.3.3   Postsynaptic potentials and the integration of incoming signals: the neuron as an information processor

By now you may have a picture of the neuron swamped by thousands of inputs. Are different inputs accorded different status? How and where are the effects of the inputs integrated? At least you should be able to answer the last part of that second question.

○   Where are the effects of the inputs integrated?

●   At the axon hillock.

This is the part of the neuron that is able to respond by either firing or not firing – the all-or-nothing response. It is probably easiest to explain integration by using the axo-dendritic synapse as an example. Figure 3.13 shows two excitatory and one inhibitory axo-dendritic synapses.

Stimulation of either 1 or 2, the excitatory synapses, causes a local depolarization at the dendritic location where the synapse occurs.

○   What is this type of postsynaptic potential called?

●   This is an excitatory postsynaptic potential (EPSP).

There will be a spread of depolarization from the point of stimulation in all directions. The extent (or strength) of the depolarization will decrease with distance from the source (the effect becomes attenuated) as is shown in Figure 3.14.

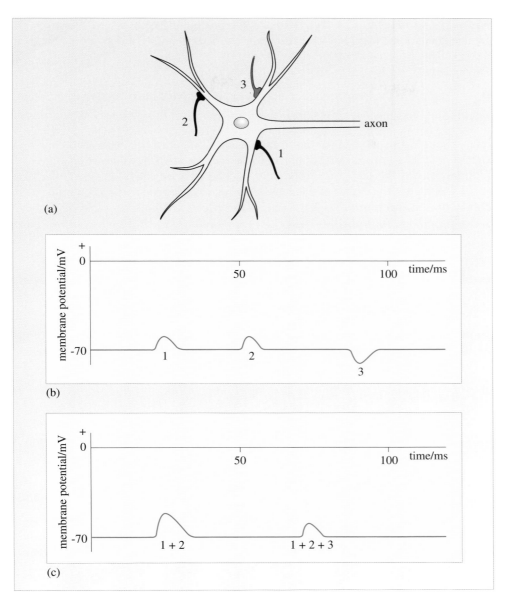

Figure 3.13   (a) Two excitatory (1 and 2) and one inhibitory (3) synapses made upon a neuron. (b) The change in membrane potential when each synapse is stimulated separately. (c) The changes in membrane potential when both synapses 1 and 2 are stimulated simultaneously and then 1, 2 and 3 are stimulated simultaneously.

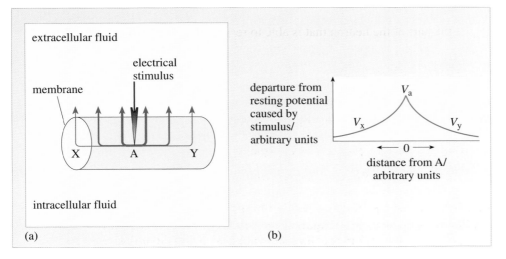

Figure 3.14   Diagram to show the change in membrane potential with distance from the postsynaptic synapse (A) with neuron 2 after receipt of an excitatory stimulus (EPSP): (a) the experimental set-up; (b) the plotted results. At the site of stimulation the depolarization is maximal and it falls as distance increases.

With respect to Figure 3.13, the effect of a given depolarization at 1 will have a greater effect at the axon hillock than would the same amount of depolarization at 2.

○ Can you say why this is so?

● 1 is closer to the axon hillock than 2 so there will have been a lesser decrease in the extent of the depolarization that reaches the axon hillock.

From Figure 3.13c you can see that if both 1 and 2 are simultaneously stimulated, their depolarizing effects will summate, resulting in a larger depolarization at the axon hillock. By the same token, should synapse 3 become active its hyperpolarizing effect will reduce the extent of the depolarization experienced at the axon hillock. This is **spatial summation**. It is the sum of the effects arising from synapses at various locations on the cell.

Imagine now a train of action potentials from neuron 1. The first one causes an EPSP as ions move across the postsynaptic membrane. The membrane potential would rapidly return to its pre-stimulation value if no further action potentials arrived at the presynaptic neuron. But with a train of action potentials the EPSP will be held and this is known as **temporal summation**.

Another factor that will affect the status of the synaptic input is the physical size of the synapse. It was briefly noted in Section 2 that some synapses are larger than others.

○ How could the physical size of the synapse affect its ability to influence the postsynaptic cell?

● A larger synapse has a greater surface area so both the amount of neurotransmitter released and the number of receptors available to receive it can be greater than for a small synapse. This means that more channels can be opened and hence more ions enter (or leave) the cell. Thus there can be a greater change in membrane potential.

So by which ever means, electrical or chemical, individual synapses have greater or lesser influence on the probability that at the axon hillock there will be sufficient depolarization to open voltage-dependent Na^+ gates and initiate an action potential.

Summary of Section 3.3

Action potentials allow a change in membrane potential to be transmitted over long distances without loss of signal strength. They can only be generated in membranes that have voltage-gated Na^+ and K^+ ion channels. These channels open briefly allowing sufficient movement of Na^+ and K^+ ions across the membrane to effect dramatic voltage changes. The local membrane change affects adjacent areas but attenuates with distance. However, the adjacent areas also possess these voltage-gated channels so that once they have been depolarized to the threshold value an action potential can be generated. Thus the signal travels along the axon. The conduction velocity of an axon depends on its diameter and on whether it is myelinated, since both these factors affect the electrical properties of the axon.

The passage of a signal across an electrical synapse can be in either direction, and there is no synaptic delay. By contrast, the chemical synapse is rectified and subject to synaptic delay. Release of neurotransmitters requires that there is first an influx of Ca^+ ions across the presynaptic membrane. After release the neurotransmitter binds to receptors on the postsynaptic membrane and, directly or indirectly, this leads to opening of channels so that ions can cross the membrane. Depending on the type of channel opened and the specific ion that can cross the postsynaptic membrane, the membrane will be depolarized (EPSP) or hyperpolarized (IPSP). The neurotransmitter is actively removed from the synaptic cleft.

The neuron acts as an information processing device. The status of different synapses varies but, by means of temporal and spatial summation, neurons can alter their output from moment to moment, thereby communicating with other neurons.

3.4 Signal to perception

We are now going to briefly highlight key aspects of the 'signal to perception' journey. In so doing, we remind you of material that has already been covered in earlier sections and, importantly, set the scene for how future blocks will be organized. This then leaves the final section to take a very different view of the active brain, that is, the one provided by modern imaging techniques.

The signal

There are many different forms of energy to which we can respond. These signals have physical properties about which we need some knowledge in order to unravel the complexities of the biological apparatus that detects and encodes the signals. So in future blocks we will describe the physics or chemistry of the signals but only to the level of detail necessary for an appreciation of the biology of the senses and the psychology of perception.

Transduction of the signal

Sensory receptors transduce the energy of the signal into electrical activity – the receptor potential. In subsequent blocks we describe the receptors and you will read about the molecular events underlying this change in membrane potential (where this is known). For the moment all we have said about receptor potentials is that they are graded, varying with the strength of the stimulus provided by the signal, and that they attenuate with distance from the site of stimulation. This means that we expect sensory receptors to be very small cells or they would not be able to use the graded receptor potential to influence the next element in the sensory pathway (which, incidentally, they do by releasing neurotransmitter). The mechanoreceptors that transduce tactile stimulation are unusual in that they are modified neurons with axons that lie in the skin and are surrounded by specialized tissue. The neuronal membrane beneath the specialized tissue responds to its adequate stimulus by generating a receptor potential and if this is sufficiently large, an action potential is initiated nearby.

○   What is the feature of the neuronal membrane that will allow it to initiate an action potential?

●   It must be an area which contains voltage-gated sodium channels.

Sensory pathways to the brain

The sensory pathways to the brain will be described in each block. Already you have observed how tactile information travels along several distinct and different pathways to reach the somatosensory cortex. Also you were introduced to two areas of the brain, the medulla and the thalamus, where different pathways synapsed. The areas where the synapses occur are called nuclei (e.g. cuneate nuclei, ventrobasal nuclei) and contain interneurons which remain within the area of the nuclei. There is also both convergence and divergence of output from the incoming axons onto the neurons that project to the next area within the brain. This means that processing can occur at each of these stages along the sensory pathways. One particularly important type of processing has been described, lateral inhibition. Lateral inhibition can explain the receptive field properties of many kinds of neurons in sensory pathways. So in each of the blocks you will learn more about sensory processing at the junctions along the pathways to the sensory cortex.

Processing in the cerebral cortex

We have seen that there are six layers in the cerebral cortex and that the functional unit is formed by a column of cells. Single cell recording makes it possible to elucidate receptive field properties of cells in the different layers of the cortex and from this to deduce how neurons might be interconnected to provide these receptive fields. There will be examples of these kinds of results in each block.

Molecular mechanisms and neuronal circuitry

At every synaptic level information is passed between neurons. The postsynaptic cell's membrane can be depolarized or hyperpolarized depending on what kind of pore is opened by the neurotransmitter. You now know something about the molecular mechanisms that bring this about but some blocks will give much more detailed information.

Synaptic potentials have similar properties to receptor potentials because they both result from the membrane altering its permeability to ions that are then able to move across the membrane in response to their concentration gradients and/or potential gradients. The magnitude of these synaptic and receptor potentials is therefore related to how many pores are opened and how many ions cross the membrane. Thus they are graded potentials that diminish in size with distance from the point of initiation in contrast to the all-or-nothing action potential. In some of the blocks there will be details of the neurotransmitters involved at particular junctions in the pathways. There will also be more details of circuitry and of interaction with other sensory modalities.

Perception

This block has only briefly touched on the difficult issues around perception. The difference between touching and being touched, the reason that we can differentiate substances based on texture (oil and water, velvet and silk), these are subjects that must wait until Block 5 for further discussion. However, we will address the issues of perception alongside sensation in all the subsequent blocks of the course, starting with hearing in Block 3.

Question 3.1

For communication over long distances, what is the important difference between Morse code (a communication code that consists of long and short pulses – 'dots and dashes') and the method of communication used by the neuron?

Question 3.2

In what ways are membrane receptors and sensory receptors similar?

Question 3.3

Which of the following statements relating to the differences between the electrical synapse and the chemical synapse is/are true?

(a) There is a wider synaptic cleft at electrical synapses.

(b) More varied signals can cross the electrical synapse, thereby increasing its capacity to process information.

(c) Electrical synapses have a longer synaptic delay than chemical synapses.

(d) Transmission across an electrical synapse is much faster than across a chemical synapse, transmission being virtually instantaneous.

Question 3.4

Imagine a neuron at its resting potential and with the distribution of ions shown in Figure 3.7a. Suddenly the membrane is made permeable to both sodium and potassium. What is the movement of ions that results and why?

Question 3.5

In terms of ionic permeability, why is it that a slight depolarization does not trigger an action potential?

Question 3.6

What is meant by the following expressions, and what is their significance in so far as speed and rate of transmission of an action potential is concerned?

(a) myelinated fibre

(b) absolute refractory period.

Question 3.7

Which of the following factors sets a limit on the rate at which action potentials may be generated?

(a) the myelin sheath

(b) the sodium pump

(c) the leakage of potassium from the cell

(d) the voltage-gated sodium channels.

Question 3.8

Which of the following influence the speed at which an action potential is transmitted along an axon?

(a) whether or not an action potential has recently been generated in the neuron;

(b) the diameter of the axon;

(c) whether or not the axon is myelinated;

(d) the rate at which Na^+ is being pumped out of the cell at the instance of passage of the action potential;

(e) the length of the axon;

(f) the balance of EPSPs and IPSPs that initiated the action potential in the first place.

Question 3.9

In Section 3.3.3 an explanation was given of how neurons that generate action potentials act as information processors. Write a brief account of how neurons without axons function as information processors.

Imaging the Active Brain

4.1 The hidden brain

We have already mentioned that it has been known since the time of the Ancient Greeks that the brain is the seat of all our sensory, cognitive and emotional functions. Although there have been periods in history when scholars mistakenly believed the heart to be the seat of human cognition, modern neuroscientists are in no doubt about the singular role the brain has in the representations of our thoughts, emotions and actions.

One of the most frustrating aspects of studying the living active brain is its inaccessibility. It is extremely well safeguarded from the minor accidents of everyday life by being encased in a hard bony skull, having the protection of thick membranes and being cushioned by cerebrospinal fluid (Figure 2.16). If, for example, you inadvertently bang your head against a cupboard door then, as painful as this may be, you are unlikely to suffer any brain damage. Such high-class protection is obviously vital, but it does make the brain difficult to study.

The usual way in which scientists investigate complex systems is to observe, manipulate, measure and interfere with key parts of the system. For obvious ethical reasons, this direct 'hands on' approach is not possible with the living human brain. Indeed, a lot of our current knowledge of the structure and operation of this remarkable organ has had to be gained from indirect methods, that is, from inferences drawn from clinical studies of patients who have suffered brain damage or from post-mortem studies. In recent years, however, the situation has been radically transformed by what has been termed the 'second revolution in medical imaging'. (As you might have guessed, the first revolution was initiated by the discovery of X-rays which dates back to 1895.) It is now possible to examine *directly* the structure and function of different regions of the normal human brain with a variety of *imaging techniques*. In other words, it is becoming feasible to observe the human brain at work and, in so doing, begin to provide answers to such fundamental questions as, 'How does the brain deal with sensory inputs?'; 'How do the sensory and motor representations interact with one another so that we can respond to our immediate environment?'; 'What is the underlying organization, for example, that provides us with memory or allows us to process language?'.

4.2 Looking inside the head: modern medical imaging techniques

One of the wonders of modern medicine is the ability to study the inside of the body without cutting it open. This seems so commonplace in the modern world that we sometimes forget that for the majority of human history this was simply impossible; the workings of the body were a complex mystery that could only be revealed by injury or death. The first medical imaging technique utilized X-ray radiation to show the position and integrity of dense objects (such as bone) within the body. Unfortunately, the technique requires the use of potentially dangerous radiation. Also, X-rays are not very good at showing detail in soft structures such as the brain. Although sophisticated X-ray systems have been recently developed which use multiple beams to generate better high-resolution pictures of the brain (X-ray computerized tomography, or CT scanning), the finest details of the brain are still hidden.

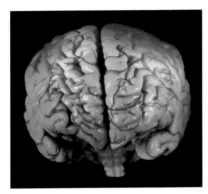

Figure 4.1   A coloured three-dimensional MRI scan of a healthy human brain seen from the front. The image is constructed from a series of consecutive experiments that provide information for individual thin slices at different angles through the brain. Computer techniques are then used to create the final three-dimensional image. This image can be rotated and structures deep within the brain can be revealed by fading out the outer layers, or by simply removing 'wedges'.

In the 1970s, a remarkable breakthrough was made which led to the development of an imaging technique – magnetic resonance imaging or MRI – that is unrivalled in its ability to provide clear images of the physical structure, or anatomy, of the brain with millimetre resolution. The technique also continues to advance as, for example, shown by the image in Figure 4.1.

CT and MRI, as already mentioned in Block 1, are **structural imaging** techniques with increasing important clinical applications. For example, they can show the presence of abnormalities and tumours with considerable clarity. These techniques are also useful for neuroscience researchers in that they can locate the exact area of damage to the brain of an individual. They can also highlight changes or variation in size as, for example, in a recent investigation in which structural MRIs of London taxi drivers revealed that they had larger hippocampi (a brain structure associated with memory) than those from a sample of the rest of the population.

However, structural imaging techniques are essentially *static* techniques, that is they provide no means of visualizing how the brain responds to the stimuli it receives on a moment-to-moment basis. To achieve this requires a new approach to imaging. This is called **functional imaging** and as you may recall, a few examples taken from this area were briefly discussed in Block 1. This section now takes a more detailed look at the important, as well as developing, area of functional imaging.

4.3   The need for new techniques to study function

The earliest tool that investigators had for studying brain function was the study of injuries to the brain. It was found that relatively small injuries to very specific regions could result in devastating deficits such as partial blindness, inability to speak or comprehend, changes in personality, the loss of memories or the inability to make new memories.

In original work carried out in the final quarter of the nineteenth century, patients who had specific temporal and frontal lobe lesions were studied by the French surgeon and anthropologist Paul Broca and the Polish born neurologist Dr Carl Wernicke who also published several highly regarded books on diseases of the nervous system. One of Broca's patients had a lesion in the frontal lobe, and could understand language, but could not speak. In contrast, one of Wernicke's patients had a lesion in the temporal lobe, and could speak, but could not comprehend language. Taken together, these two patients presented compelling evidence that the brain was organized in a *modular* way, with different areas performing different functions. There are, however, significant problems in using the consequences of injuries and lesions to infer functional localization. You may wish to think about what these could be before reading on.

One problem with this line of research, and perhaps the most obvious, is that it is necessary to find a living individual who has suffered an injury in the specific part of the brain that is of interest. Secondly, lesions are never simple injuries that are confined to one specific brain area. They may cross several regional boundaries and damage tracts (white matter) that carry information from one part of the brain to another. There may also be unseen damage, undetected even when using modern structural imaging techniques, to another part of the brain that has arisen from the primary lesion. Thirdly, do we know that if everyone had the same lesion, in the same area of the brain, that they would lose the same function? Finally, we know that the brain has amazing properties of re-organization after injury. Often stroke victims will have significant paralysis after the event, but are able to recover most, if not all, function after days, weeks or months. The brain is often able to 're-wire' itself so that important functions are regained. So, if we are studying functional deficits in patients with lesions we do not know if some of this cortical re-organization might have already taken place.

At the turn of the nineteenth century, scientists were also beginning to carry out detailed anatomical studies of post-mortem brains. Using microscopy and staining techniques, Brodmann (see Section 5, Block 1) was able to identify 47 anatomically distinct regions of the human cerebral cortex and later studies increased this number to over 200 areas. But once again there are problems in relating these cytoarchitectural maps to brain function. It is not clear that all of the anatomically-defined areas have specific and different functional roles and so there are serious doubts about the utility of cytoarchitectural maps in describing cortical functional organization.

Injury and post-mortem studies along with other 'classical' neuroscience techniques can provide important information on the working of the human brain but, as discussed, there can be serious problems in interpretation. Basically, this is because they are *indirect* tools. Ideally we would like to be able to get through the several millimetres of scalp and skull to investigate the brain of normal individuals, without causing distress or being sued for damages. In addition, a way is needed of studying the brain in the 'intermediate range'; that is, to bridge the gap between the microscopic – the investigation of single neurons, and the macroscopic – the study of the behavioural properties of an entire human being. In other words we want to be able to monitor the activity of *discrete populations* of neurons since it is their combined integrative action that produces cognition.

4.4 Functional imaging of the brain

Functional imaging has become increasingly associated with experiments whose aim is to map sensory, motor and cognitive functions to distinct anatomical regions of the brain and it is this particular aspect that we focus on here. It should be remembered, however, that there are also expanding applications in visualizing other areas of function of the human body such as those involved with the cardiac cycle or metabolic activity in tissue.

In any functional imaging study it is important to be aware of the *resolving power*, that is in both space and time, of the technique that is being used. Resolving power in space is referred to as **spatial resolution,** and that in time as **temporal resolution**. For the various functional imaging techniques these quantities are often the subject of debate, if not controversy, and different definitions arise depending on the technique that is being used. Nevertheless, it is still possible to make some useful generalizations.

The classic definition of spatial resolution relates to the distance that two objects must be separated so that they can be distinguished as two objects instead of one. For functional imaging we can think (in simple terms) of this definition as being the smallest distance over which distinct and reliable information relating to local brain activity can be established. Temporal resolution relates to the timescale over which functional images can be measured.

4.4.1 Direct techniques: MEG and EEG

Ideally, because we know that the brain is essentially an electrical device, with information conveyed from neuron to neuron as electrical impulses, we would like a technique that could *directly* measure the electrical activity of the brain.

Figure 4.2   A modern geodesic sensor net that forms part of an EEG system.

Electroencephalography

One of the earliest attempts to measure the direct activity associated with brain function involved attaching electrodes to the scalp of a volunteer and then recording the electrical currents from the brain. This is known as **electroencephalography** (**EEG**). EEG relies on the fact that currents within the brain can 'leak' to the surface through the membranes, skull and scalp. The skull is actually an electrical insulator and, as a consequence, the current has to travel through normal holes and sutures in the skull. The first human EEG was measured in 1929 by Hans Berger, and it was noted that the normal EEG contained rhythms of various frequencies with the alpha rhythms of spontaneous brain activity (8–13 Hz) being dominant over the posterior part of the brain. It was also noted that the normal pattern of measured electrical activity could be severely distorted by illnesses such as epilepsy.

The earliest EEG systems used only one or two electrodes attached to the scalp, but modern systems use considerably more electrodes (Figure 4.2) and improved electrode placement technology means that such systems can be attached to the head of a volunteer in less than 15 minutes by a trained technician. These dense-array systems allow the EEG to be measured with high resolution. EEG is relatively inexpensive with modern dense-array systems costing in the order of £50 000.

In one form of EEG investigation, the electrical activity associated with the response of an individual at different times following a particular form of stimulus is plotted over the scalp as a coloured map (see Figure 4.3). This can be viewed as a form of functional imaging since it allows 'general' areas of the brain to be identified which are involved in the response to the stimulus. However, the technique is limited in that the images obtained, which are often plotted on a MRI model of the head, are restricted to the brain's surface.

○   Can you suggest another limitation?

●   As already mentioned, electrical currents generated within the brain due to neuronal activity 'leak' to the surface through membranes, skull and scalp. In particular, the skull is an electrical insulator and so electrical current can only pass through holes and sutures. Thus an observed area of maximum signal could be displaced from the underlying generating area in the cortex.

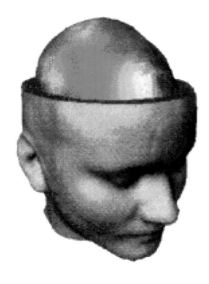

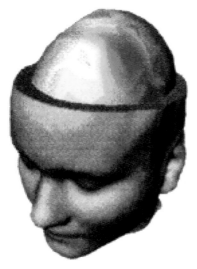

Figure 4.3   EEG results reveal what is going on in the brain of a volunteer who is given the task of deciding whether a letter that is displayed on a screen in front of her is located in the same position as any one of three letters that she has seen previously. Brighter colours (moving towards red) represent a higher degree of brain activity. The upper image shows a strong electrical signal passing across the frontal cortex of the right hemisphere some 320 milliseconds after a new letter has appeared on the screen. This is associated with 'comparing'. The lower image, taken 140 milliseconds later, shows that the measured electrical activity has now moved to the left hemisphere. This is associated with 'updating'; that is entering the location of the new letter into working memory ready for the task to continue.

An important advantage of EEG is that it can measure brain activity at a very rapid rate. The typical timescale of brain activity is in the millisecond range and, with the correct electronics, EEG is perfectly capable of recording at this rate or faster. Thus, at least potentially, EEG can provide *timing information* about processes in the brain associated with mental operations such as those involved with perception, attention, memory, language and emotion.

EEG relies on measurements that are taken 'outside the brain'. To pinpoint the distinct site, or sites, where activity *within the brain* responsible for the observed measurements is taking place, requires what is known as the *'inverse problem'* to be solved. In fact, in strictly mathematical terms, this problem is impossible to solve! It will always turn out that an infinite number of arrangements involving combinations of cortical current generators will be able to generate a given set of external scalp measurements. This is known as *non-uniqueness*. Fortunately, if additional information (referred to as *constraints*) is added to the problem, such as limiting the number of current generators that can be active at any one instant of time, then a solution can be found (although there is no absolute guarantee that it will be correct). It is also essential to supply some model for how the electrical current from a particular part of the cortex will leak to the surface of the scalp. A problem with EEG is that this information is only known approximately and this leads to limitations in present day investigations. In general, the spatial resolution of EEG is often not well defined. Overall, however, despite the difficulties, it is possible using sophisticated computer software packages to work out the number, location and strength of current generators within the brain that give rise to the electrical potentials measured on the scalp in an EEG investigation and to gain direct functional information. Figure 4.4 is an example of an EEG recording of the human brain.

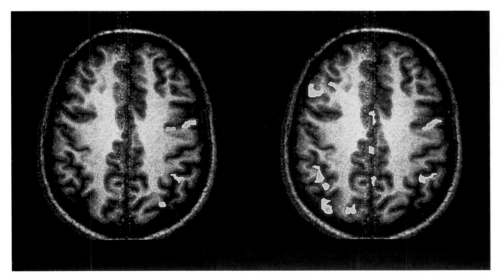

Figure 4.4   An EEG investigation of brain activity measured during mathematical problem solving superimposed on horizontal MRI brain scans. On the left is the brain of a person reciting multiplication tables, whilst on the right the subject is performing repeated subtractions. Active brain areas are located in orange.

Magnetoencephalography

A related, direct, functional imaging techniques is **magnetoencephalography** (**MEG**). The results from a typical MEG study are shown in Figure 4.5 and show how specific regions of the brain 'light up' when a person is involved in a particular task. Like EEG, measurements are taken outside the brain but here the measurements are of magnetic fields detected close to the scalp. The technique is able to detect and locate the very weak magnetic fields associated with the electrical currents caused by neuronal activity (Box 4.1). Since it is magnetic fields that are measured, the technique is sometimes referred to as magnetic source imaging (MSI). As you can see in Figure 4.5, the areas within the brain of an adult volunteer that were activated by touching the fingers as well as the thumb of one hand can be located with considerable precision. It is now common practice in functional imaging for the MEG results to be projected onto a three-dimensional MRI reconstruction of the subject's brain so that it is possible to show the sources of brain activity derived from MEG with respect to anatomical information obtained from MRI. (You may wish to compare the MEG results in Figure 4.5 with those shown in Block 1, Figure 5.3, which relate to a particular type of congenital hand deformity.)

○ From your study of the anatomical pathways, which areas of the brain would you expect to 'light up' when the fingers and thumb of one hand are touched?

● The dorsal-column-medial-lemniscal (DCML) pathway projects firstly to the medulla, then to the contra-lateral thalamus and finally to the somatosensory cortex (only the latter brain area is shown in Figure 4.5).

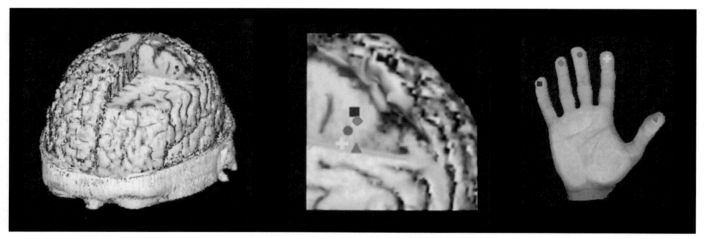

Figure 4.5 The representation, as determined by means of MEG, of the fingers and thumb of the right hand in the somatosensory cortex of an adult volunteer. The responses of the fingers and thumb to tactile stimulation (with skin contact over an area of 28 mm²) are colour-coded and displayed on a three-dimensional MRI reconstruction of the subject's brain with the image oriented so that the subject is looking out from the paper.

Similar computer techniques and inverse-problem strategies are used in MEG. However, the big advantage of MEG is that the magnetic fields originating from neuronal electric currents pass straight through the brain, skull and scalp to the detectors. It is not necessary to know the conductivity 'pathway' which, as already mentioned, is a very difficult part of the EEG inverse-problem. At least in theory, this gives MEG the potential to locate specific areas of brain activity with high spatial resolution and, indeed, many experiments (for example, see Figure 4.5) have shown that for cortical current sources close to the surface of the brain, neuronal activity can be localized to within 2 mm, or less. MEG is not so sensitive to sources deep within the brain. This is because magnetic fields reduce rapidly with distance from the detectors (in fact, they depend on an inverse-cubic relationship). However, most of the cortex is within the detectable range of most systems. A particular problem of MEG is that current sources that are orientated at 90 degrees to the surface of the scalp cannot be detected by MEG. Fortuitously, the cortex is constructed in complex folds so that not much of the brain is oriented in this 'silent' manner.

Box 4.1   Magnetoencephalography: measuring brain activity using SQUIDs

Every electrical current generates an associated magnetic field, and it was realized in the 1960s that it should be possible to measure the magnetic fields arising from electrical activity in the human body. However, there are serious technical difficulties to overcome, not the least of which is that signals from the human brain are extremely weak. The magnetic fields to be measured are typically 100 million times smaller than the Earth's magnetic field and 1 million times smaller than the magnetic fields which are generated from various sources in the urban environment.

In the late 1960s, James Zimmerman introduced the idea of a superconducting quantum interference device (SQUID) which is one of the most sensitive measuring devices known and certainly the most sensitive magnetic field detector. Because they are superconducting devices, SQUIDs only work when immersed in liquid helium at a temperature of −269 °C. The quantum mechanical principles that underlie SQUID technology are complex, but essentially a

SQUID consists of a small ring of superconducting material, a few millimetres across. In the world of quantum mechanics, if the external magnetic field through this loop changes, an electrical current will be induced in the loop that can be detected using external electronics.

The sensitivity of the SQUID is easily good enough to measure brain activity, and by using magnetically shielded rooms and other noise-reducing strategies, MEG systems can be constructed which measure brain activity, but reject the signals from more distant objects such as the heart, or buses and cars outside the building. Modern multi-channel systems have large liquid-helium vacuum flasks containing 150 SQUID detectors (Figure 4.6). Compared to EEG, SQUID systems are expensive; a typical, fully-operational system can cost between £1–1.5 million, and the running costs are not trivial due to the liquid helium requirements. Nonetheless, despite the expense, MEG is now established as a very powerful tool in neuroscience research.

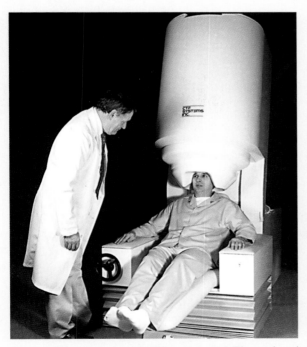

Figure 4.6   A modern MEG system. (a) The patient is prepared for the scan procedure. (b) A close up of the apparatus. The gap between the surface of the head, which is at room temperature, and the SQUID coils which are at −269 °C, is only a matter of a few millimetres.

○ What other very important feature would you wish to know about in using MEG as a functional imaging technique?

● It is important to know how quickly the images can be recorded; that is, the temporal resolution.

In fact, MEG systems are similar to those for EEG in that recordings can be made on a millisecond timescale. Thus, MEG is well suited to providing timing information about cognitive processes in the brain.

There is one final comment to be made concerning both EEG and MEG. The fact that signals can be measured suggests that when a particular area of the brain is performing a specific task, a large population of neurons fire in synchrony. If this were not the case then the electrical current from a small number of cells would be too small to be measured. Furthermore, it is as if the 'importance' of a particular task or stimulus is represented by the size of the synchronously firing population of neurons. However, this is still a controversial area with some neuroscientists claiming that visual performance (especially the ability to detect very weak stimuli) is actually based on no more than a handful of neurons; sometimes even a single neuron could be sufficient. Nonetheless, strong evidence is emerging that points to synchronous firing of neurons as being essential in perception.

○ How would you reconcile the suggestion that a weak visual stimulus involves only a handful of neurons whilst perception involves a large population firing in synchrony?

● Figure 2.37 shows how, by divergence, one sensory cell can influence an array of cortical cells.

4.4.2 Indirect techniques: PET and fMRI

The metabolism of the brain is highly complex, and there is a constant high demand for metabolic fuels, specifically glucose and oxygen, which have to be present. It is known that when a region of the brain is 'working hard' there are local changes in brain metabolism which are associated in some way with the energy requirements of the enhanced neuronal activity. The metabolic changes include an increase in the amount of blood flowing to the region, increased oxygen content of this blood and changes in brain cell glucose consumption. Two major functional imaging techniques rely on the ability to detect these types of change in local brain metabolism. They are **positron emission tomography (PET)** and **functional magnetic resonance imaging (fMRI)** which, as its name implies, is an extension of the structural MRI technique. On a historical note, it is worth noting that the idea of linking blood flow to brain function is by no means new. The English physiologists Charles Roy and Charles Sherrington suggested the connection as early as 1890.

PET is regarded as one of the first true functional imaging techniques and was developed in the 1970s. Early landmark investigations produced some surprising results. Although functionally-induced local increases in blood flow and alterations in the rate of glucose consumption were observed, it was found that oxygen concentrations did not decrease as expected, but rather increased. In other words, the enhanced supply of oxygen due to the increased blood flow was *more* than the local demand. The reasons for this behaviour are still not fully understood. However, the oversupply of oxygen which is sufficiently large to be detectable, turns out to be very useful for functional imaging purposes.

○   Which cells are believed to activate the local capillaries to dilate thus increasing blood flow?

●   Glial cells, specifically astrocytes.

It must be said that the precise nature of the coupling between neuronal activity and the types of local metabolic change that can be detected by PET and fMRI is still an issue of some controversy. Nonetheless there is a strong view that there is a relationship and that these techniques can be taken to be sensitive to activity in the brain that *correlates* with neuronal activity. However, PET and fMRI, unlike EEG and MEG, cannot be taken as *direct* monitors of brain function.

Positron emission tomography

PET works using a radioactive tracer mechanism. A wide variety of substances, that have been specifically labelled with radioactive isotopes, have been used for scanning purposes. These are either inhaled by, or injected into, a subject and within a minute or so will be present in the brain. All the tracer substances have radioactive labels (for example ^{13}N, ^{15}O or ^{18}F) which emit positrons during their radioactive decay; hence the name of the technique. Radioactive-labelled water ($H_2^{15}O$) is commonly used, for example, in functional studies based on blood flow. It is the emission of positrons, followed by the subsequent emission of gamma-rays, that underlies the construction of a PET image (see Box 4.2).

A typical PET experiment involves a volunteer being administered, say $H_2^{15}O$, and then a *resting* (or baseline) image is recorded after a few minutes by the PET scanner. The volunteer is then subjected to some form of stimulus and the scanner is now used to record a *stimulated* image. The basic idea is that there will be a preferential take up of radioisotope, and hence more positron decay, in regions of the volunteer's brain that are activated by the stimulus. By subtracting the resting scan from the stimulated scan, those areas of the brain that have responded to the stimulus will be highlighted. PET images resulting from a study of acute pain are shown in Figure 4.7.

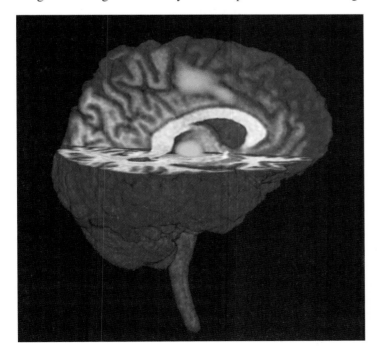

Figure 4.7   Pain intensity-related activation of the thalamus and anterior cingulate cortex. Positron emission tomography of cerebral blood flow in normal healthy volunteers reveals that painful heat stimuli produce activation of a number of brain regions including the thalamus and anterior cingulate cortex (activation in orange on blue MRI image). These regions (and many others) were activated in direct proportion to the intensity of pain that subjects perceived, indicating that sensory dimensions of the pain experience are processed in a highly distributed fashion.

Box 4.2   Positrons and PET images

The discovery of the positron as a new particle came about through cosmic ray investigations in 1932. Positrons have the same mass as an electron but have a positive, rather than negative, charge. Positrons are emitted during the nuclear decay of certain unstable radioisotopes. This decay effectively stabilizes the nucleus by converting a proton into a neutron. Thus, for example, the oxygen radioisotope ^{15}O which has a mass number of 15, corresponding to 8 protons and 7 neutrons in the nucleus, is converted to the more stable nitrogen isotope ^{15}N, which has 7 protons and 8 neutrons in its nucleus. For all of the radioisotopes used in PET studies, the elements formed by positron decay are stable; that is they are not radioactive.

A positron will travel away from the nucleus from which it has been emitted and as it passes through matter (in the present context the brain) it will lose kinetic energy. In fact, within a few millimetres it will come to rest and at this point it will react violently with the closest electron. This is called annihilation because the entire rest mass of both particles is instantaneously converted into energy such that two gamma-rays (also

called photons) are emitted in almost exactly opposite directions (Figure 4.8). The 'line' along which the emission occurs can be along any direction in space.

A functional neuroimaging PET scanner is designed so that the head of a volunteer can be surrounded by an array of gamma-ray detectors (Figure 4.9). Fast electronics is then used to look for pairs of gamma-rays that are *simultaneously* emitted in opposite directions; this is referred to as coincidence detection. The recording of such an event means that annihilation must have occurred along the line joining the two detectors. With many detectors, and the recording of many events, it is possible to work back – using a technique called 'filtered back projection' – to form a three-dimensional image of the amount of gamma-ray emission at each point in the brain. This is often superimposed on a MRI scan as in Figure 4.7. It should be noted that the site of gamma emission (corresponding to positron annihilation) that is imaged will be at the most a few millimetres from the site of the original positron emission from the radioisotope.

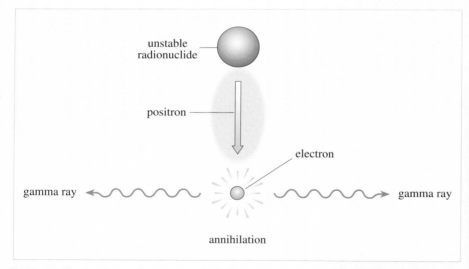

Figure 4.8   The emission of a positron leading to eventual annihilation.

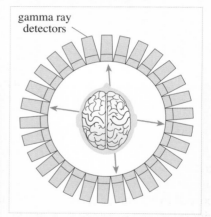

Figure 4.9   A schematic view of the arrangement for a PET scan of the brain.

As with all functional imaging techniques, PET does have some disadvantages. Firstly, it involves the administration of a radioisotope and, although the doses are low and considered relatively safe, there are obvious health concerns about introducing any radioactivity into the body. Secondly, the amount of measured signal is usually quite low in a PET scan and as a consequence it is necessary to average the results from several repeat scans in order to get statistically meaningful results. However, the amount of radioactivity that can be given to any one subject is strictly limited and so the scans to be averaged often have to come from several individuals as in the example in Figure 4.7. This is not ideal since one aim of functional imaging is to provide activation maps on an *individual* basis. Thirdly, both the resting and stimulated scans can take several minutes to acquire and so this means that it is not possible to use PET to track brain activity at the millisecond level as is possible with MEG and EEG. With modern equipment, regional blood flow in the whole brain can be monitored, at best, with a temporal resolution of the order of 40 s. One further disadvantage, although mainly in terms of comparison to fMRI, is the spatial resolution that can be achieved. PET can only pinpoint areas within the brain in which there is a local activity to about 5 mm and at this level of resolution PET images appear quite 'blurred'.

○ Can you suggest why there is an 'absolute' limit of spatial resolution for the PET technique irrespective of how 'state-of-the-art' the PET scanner may be?

● The location of the radioisotope is taken as the site which correlates with neuronal activity. However, the site that is imaged is different and is that which corresponds to positron annihilation. Thus the distance between the site of the radioisotope that emits the positron and the site at which the positron is annihilated provides an absolute limit in the spatial resolution of PET scan images. Typically, this distance is of the order of a few millimetres.

As a final point it must, of course, also be mentioned that PET investigations need a supply of radioisotopes and these are often short-lived; for example the lifetime of ^{15}O is measured in minutes rather than hours. A local cyclotron to produce the radioisotope, plus facilities to handle them, is essential.

Functional magnetic resonance imaging

Both structural and functional MRI rely on the same basic physical principles. Indeed, one of the big advantages of fMRI is that it can be carried out using the modern clinical scanners that are installed in large hospitals. This means that the cost of fMRI can be relatively low compared to other functional imaging techniques since it can be shared with clinical partners.

Although MRI does not require any ionising radiation (such as X-rays), it does require a subject to be placed in a very strong magnetic field. Typically, the magnetic field is greater by four orders of magnitude (10 000 times greater) than the strength of the Earth's own magnetic field at the poles. This strong magnetic field is needed to influence the behaviour of the nuclei of all of the hydrogen atoms in the part of the body to be investigated. A modern clinical MRI scanner is shown in Figure 4.10 (overleaf). (Interestingly, we do not have any senses specialized to enable us to detect magnetic fields so are unaffected (perceptually) by this signal. By contrast, birds, notably pigeons, can detect the Earth's magnetic field and use it as an orientation cue, in much the same way that we use the visual cues of the sun or stars for navigation.)

Figure 4.10 A clinical MRI scanner showing the magnet with its large diameter horizontal bore in the background. The patient is made comfortable on the examination table which is then pushed into the magnet.

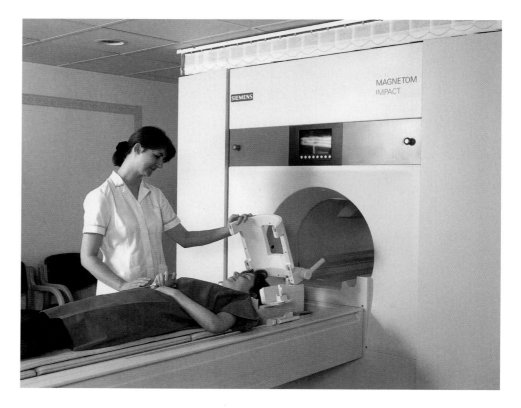

Hydrogen atoms are largely abundant in the body, including the brain, because of their presence in the major constituent of tissue: water. They are also present in fat and protein. The nucleus of each hydrogen atom consists of just one proton and this particle has a special property called *nuclear spin*. Roughly speaking, it is acceptable to visualize a proton as an electrically-charged sphere that *spins* on its own axis. As with any spinning charge, this generates a magnetic field and so this means that a proton has properties that to some extent mimic those of a tiny bar magnet. Normally, in the absence of a large applied magnetic field these 'proton magnets' point in random directions. However, in the presence of a magnetic field there are only two possibilities available to the proton magnets; they can align along the field or against it. In fact, it turns out that there is always a slight excess of proton magnets that align with the field since this is a lower energy situation. Thus for the brain scan, once a subject is immersed in the magnetic field of the MRI scanner *all* of the proton magnets will be in one of two orientations or states; this can be referred to as the 'equilibrium situation'.

This equilibrium situation can be disturbed – so that there is change between the two states – by applying electromagnetic radiation in the radiofrequency region; typically in the range 40 MHz to 100 MHz. The exact frequency required depends on the magnitude of the magnetic field but the relationship is a simple linear one such that, for example, doubling the magnetic field will require the frequency to be doubled. The key point, although we shall not go into detail, is that the disturbance caused by applying the radiofrequency radiation can be monitored, so that a signal with an intensity related to the 'number of proton nuclei that are disturbed' can be measured at the appropriate frequency. If it is arranged that different parts of, say, the brain experience different magnetic fields then each part will respond to a different irradiation frequency; in other words signals coming from different parts of the brain will be distinguishable from one another (Box 4.3). Although technically complex, it is possible to build on this idea of 'frequency encoding' so that all of the signals can be built up into a three-dimensional image.

Box 4.3   A one-dimensional MRI experiment

Figure 4.11 shows, in schematic form, the results of a one-dimensional imaging experiment based on a rectangular vessel containing water. In *Experiment 1* the vessel is bathed in a strong, uniform, applied magnetic field. The plot of signal intensity versus frequency of irradiation consists of just a single sharp response because *all* of the protons will be disturbed from their equilibrium situation at the same frequency – no matter where they are in the sample.

In *Experiment 2*, the magnetic field at the centre of the rectangular vessel is the same as in the first

experiment, but an additional magnetic field has also been superimposed. This field, which is referred to as a magnetic field gradient, has the effect of:

- increasing the overall magnetic field in a linear fashion in moving left from the centre, and
- decreasing the overall magnetic field in a linear fashion in moving right from the centre.

(It should be noted that in the diagram the magnitude of the change in overall magnetic field is exaggerated for display purposes; typically in MRI scans magnetic

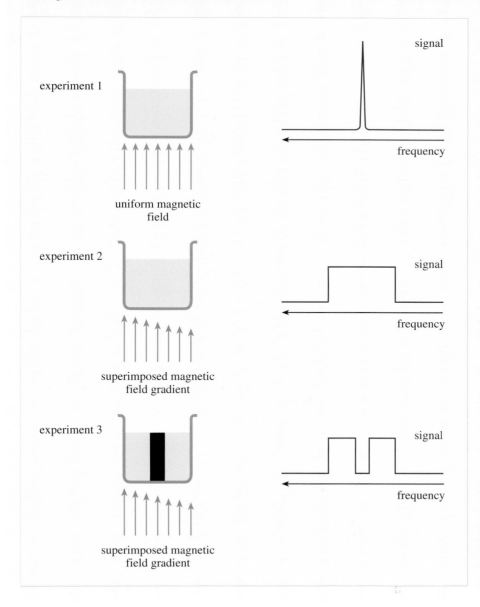

Figure 4.11   Three experiments that demonstrate one-dimensional magnetic resonance imaging; full details are given in the text.

field gradients contribute no more than a small percentage to the main magnetic field.)

The plot of signal intensity versus frequency is now no longer a single sharp line. In effect, it is a whole series of these lines each at its own distinct frequency corresponding to a particular value of overall magnetic field. Essentially, the response is a one-dimensional image of the rectangular vessel. The total signal intensity in *Experiment 1* and *2* will be the same under the same conditions. So the response, as drawn for *Experiment 2*, is that obtained by adding together the results of a number of repeat experiments.

Experiment 3 is the same as that for *Experiment 2* except that a strip of material, *not containing hydrogen atoms*, is placed at the centre of the vessel. The plot of signal intensity versus frequency now shows a 'gap' corresponding to the strip and serves to emphasize that it is a one-dimensional image that is being measured.

The radiofrequency irradiation that is used in MRI is provided in short bursts, typically with durations of microseconds, and these are referred to as pulses. Furthermore, not just one but a series of pulses is used in sequence. One major feature of this approach is that by careful timing of the sequences it is possible to introduce *contrast* into the image; that is, to distinguish clearly between different parts of the anatomy. At the heart of this behaviour lies the fact that the rate at which proton magnets return to their equilibrium situation after being irradiated depends very much on the type of tissue in which the hydrogen atoms are present. Thus, for example, in *Experiment 3* in Figure 4.11 if one compartment contained white matter and the other cerebrospinal fluid of the brain, then it would be possible to significantly change the relative intensities of the signals from the two compartments simply by changing the timing of the pulse sequence. This is a very important aspect of MRI.

If we now turn to fMRI, the key aim is to highlight those areas within a conventional MRI scan of the brain that show activity in response to some form of stimulus. This aim can be realized using a number of techniques (the level of sophistication is increasing rapidly) but one of the most important is based upon the detection of local increases in blood flow in activated areas of the brain.

○   Can you recall from earlier discussion, what happens to the consumption of oxygen in these areas?

●   Perhaps surprisingly, the uptake of oxygen does not increase to the same extent. In other words, the supply of oxygen outstrips demand.

Oxygen is transported around the body in the bloodstream in the form of oxyhaemoglobin. Haemoglobin itself consists of a protein, globin, to which is attached four haem units each of which contains an atom of iron in the form of the ion, Fe^{2+}. When oxyhaemoglobin gives up oxygen, the resulting deoxyhaemoglobin is compartmentalized in the red blood cells. Oxy- and deoxy-haemoglobin are not only chemically different but they also differ in their magnetic properties. In particular, deoxyhaemoglobin is paramagnetic and this means that the red blood cells themselves tend to behave as 'miniature bar magnets' and so cause slight distortions in the overall magnetic field experienced by nearby tissue. The amount of distortion will determine, depending on the pulse sequence used, the 'brightness' associated with this tissue in the MR image.

So, under conditions of normal cerebral blood flow there will be a particular ratio of the oxy- to deoxy- forms of haemoglobin in the blood (Figure 4.12a) and in an appropriately constructed MR scan the nearby tissue will appear in the image with a

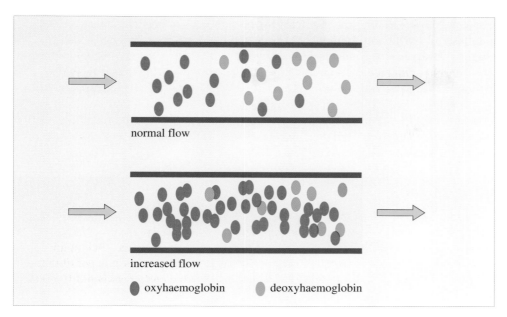

Figure 4.12   Schematic views of the oxyhaemoglobin and deoxyhaemoglobin content of blood during (a) normal and (b) increased flow in the brain.

certain brightness. However, with enhanced blood flow due to functional activity, the oxyhaemoglobin content of the blood is increased and the local concentration of deoxyhaemoglobin is correspondingly decreased (Figure 4.12b). As a result there is slightly less distortion to the overall magnetic field experienced by nearby tissue and, under the conditions of the pulse sequence used, this tissue will appear relatively more bright in the image. This is referred to by the acronym BOLD which stands for blood oxygenation level-dependent contrast.

Given that blood makes up a small fraction, typically less than 7%, of the total mass of the brain, then the local signal changes that occur in fMRI during activity in the brain are always going to be small. Nonetheless, even in the earliest applications they could be adequately detected (Figure 4.13). This gives fMRI the advantage that *single* subjects can always be investigated and, since there is no need for radioactive tracers as in PET, experiments can be repeated many times on the same subject.

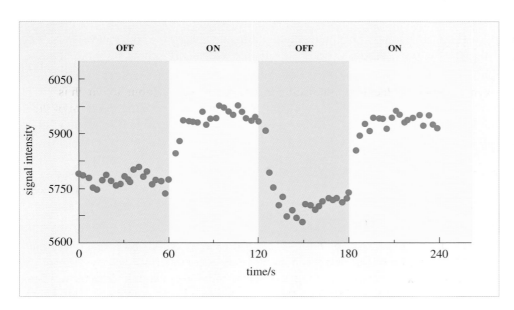

Figure 4.13   Some of the first fMRI results based on the detection of localized changes in blood flow were designed to investigate brain activity during visual stimulation. This set of results shows the changes in signal activity within a small area (approximately 60 mm²) of the visual cortex near the calcarine fissure during darkness (stimulation *off*) and exposure to a pattern of flashing light (stimulation *on*) for a normal volunteer. In the experiment, the volunteer wore light-proof goggles with each eyepiece containing an array of programmable red light-emitting diodes. Images were collected every three seconds. The signal change detected between '*on*' and '*off*' stimulation is about 3% for this particular volunteer.

Extremely fast scanning rates, at least by the standards of normal clinical MRI, are required for fMRI. Ideally the *whole* brain should be scanned for changes in intensity every few seconds. It was not until the 1990s that scanner technology was able to deliver this ideal. Even so, the spatial resolution of the images has to be compromised to deliver these fast scan rates, and a modern fMRI experiment will scan the brain every three seconds with a spatial resolution of 3 mm. As a consequence the 'structural part' of the image can appear blurred. Functional results are thus often superimposed on a high-resolution MRI scan to give a better idea of where the activation is located (Figure 4.14).

Figure 4.14 The results of a functional MRI experiment in which a subject is shown a simple moving visual stimulus. Statistical analysis is used to locate those regions in the brain which show a significant change in image intensity. These results are then superimposed, in the form of a colour overlay, on high-resolution structural images to give better definition of anatomical location.

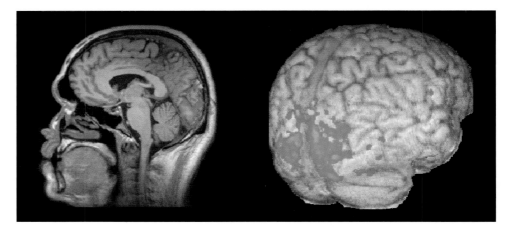

It should be remembered that it is blood flow response which is taken to be a measure of function in fMRI. This response is not immediate and takes time to build up; this is for example, evident in Figure 4.13 between the regions of '*off – on*' stimulation where it takes a few seconds for the maximum response to be achieved during *on* stimulation. The temporal resolution of fMRI is limited by how quickly *measurable changes* can be detected; typically this can be of the order of a second, although recently it has been possible in very sensitive experiments to distinguish between cortical events separated by as little as 200 milliseconds.

The factors of good spatial resolution, reasonable temporal resolution, relatively low cost and the fact that no invasive chemicals are used, have meant that fMRI is at present the most popular of the functional imaging techniques. It should also be remarked that *all* parts of the brain are sampled with *equal* spatial resolution (as is also the case with PET but not, as you should recall, MEG). Finally, computing power is essential in fMRI and major advances continue to be made such that it is becoming feasible to record *and display*, with high spatial resolution, what is going on in a volunteer's brain on a timescale of a few seconds (Figure 4.15).

4.4.3 Experimental strategy

Good experimental design is an essential ingredient for a successful functional imaging experiment. The phrase, 'designing the **stimulus paradigm**' is often used in this context. As might be expected, paradigm design is not straightforward and so just a brief overview is given here.

One common stimulus presentation pattern used in PET and fMRI is that of regular periods (or epochs) of rest and stimulus; these are often referred to as the control and the task states. The duration of the periods need to be long enough to accommodate, for example, the blood flow response. During the task state a number of images are

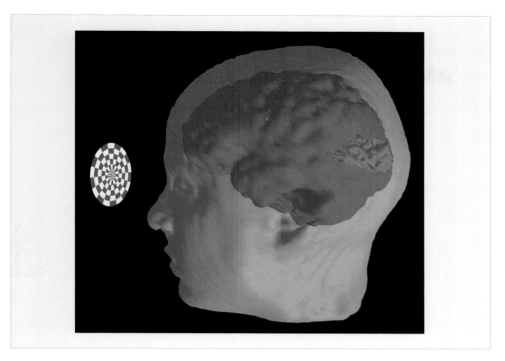

Figure 4.15 This three-dimensional image is the result of an fMRI visual stimulation experiment in which a volunteer views a whirling pattern. The brain is visualized as a translucent image and the area of activity in the visual cortex is 'highlighted': the image can be rotated and manipulated at will. Despite the huge amount of information that must be processed in order to construct the final three-dimensional animation, it can now be completed with modern computer processing power in a matter of seconds and in the future probably even shorter times. Volunteers will almost be able to see themselves thinking!

recorded; if you look back to Figure 4.13 you will see an example of this. The number of repeats of the rest/stimulus cycle depends on how difficult it is to obtain reliable data that clearly identify the part of the brain active during the task.

○ Can you suggest a practical limitation on the time of the experiment?

● It will depend on how long the subject can comfortably remain still: any movement of the head will spoil the image. (There is also the possibility that the subject may become too 'familiar' with the stimulus and so lose concentration.)

Instead of a period of stimulation, it is possible to use a single event. This is a typical approach in MEG studies. In this case the stimulus can be generated at irregular time intervals but always with the MEG recording synchronized with the stimulus. In this way any local brain response will be enhanced when the average is taken. Any other activity, not connected with the stimulus, will have a random effect on each MEG recording and so will cancel out on averaging.

The choice of stimulus is also critical. Ideally, it should be selected so as to isolate as best as possible a limited number of 'brain activities'; subtraction of rest from task state images then clearly indicates the region (or regions) of the brain associated with the particular task. However, such unambiguity is often difficult to achieve particularly when dealing with cognitive functions such as memory. In this case, for example, the stimulus may be visual but the subject must indicate their response by some form of motor action. The brain activity associated with the visual and motor responses must be allowed for in some way. One approach is to perform a subsequent experiment which involves a similar stimulus and response, but not the cognitive task performed in the original experiment. Paradigm design can become very complex! It is also worth noting that rapid-imaging fMRI scanners tend to be very noisy in their operation and this presents difficulties in ensuring that aural stimuli are heard properly. Furthermore, it makes unambiguous detection of activations in the auditory areas of the brain very difficult.

Question 4.1

What would you say are the key features of the MEG results shown in Figure 4.5?

Question 4.2

Suppose that you had to construct a table that *concisely* described the key features of the four functional imaging techniques: EEG, MEG, PET and fMRI. What *headings* would you use for your table?

Question 4.3

Each functional imaging technique has its own distinct advantages and disadvantages. Suppose that it is possible to design a new functional imaging technique that combines just the 'best' features of each technique. What would these features be?

Summary of Section 4

Modern imaging techniques can be classified as either structural or functional. Structural imaging techniques (CT, MRI) are essentially static techniques that provide images of the physical structure, or anatomy, of different parts of the body. Functional imaging techniques, in studies of the brain, aim to map sensory, motor and cognitive functions to specific regions of this organ. In functional imaging, spatial resolution can be considered to relate to the smallest distance over which distinct and reliable information relating to brain activity can be established. Temporal resolution relates to the timescale over which functional images can be measured.

There are four main functional imaging techniques: electroencephalography (EEG), magnetoencephalography (MEG), positron emission tomography (PET) and functional magnetic resonance imaging (fMRI). MEG and EEG are direct techniques since they measure, respectively, magnetic fields and electric currents associated with neuronal activity. PET and fMRI are indirect techniques since they measure local changes in the metabolism of the brain, for example associated with increased blood flow, that are taken to correlate with activity in the brain. PET involves a volunteer being administered a substance that is specifically labelled with a radioactive isotope that decays by positron emission. A popular fMRI technique is based on BOLD: blood oxygenation level-dependent contrast.

Spatial resolutions of the order of a few millimetres can be achieved for MEG, PET and fMRI. In the case of PET and fMRI, all parts of the brain are sampled with equal spatial resolution whereas using MEG spatial resolution degrades for regions deeper within the brain. The spatial resolution for EEG is not well defined. MEG and EEG recordings can be taken on a millisecond timescale. For PET temporal resolution is at best of the order of 40 s, whereas for fMRI it can be reduced to the order of a second.

Designing suitable stimulus paradigms is an important part of functional imaging and the choice of stimulus itself can be critical. A common stimulus presentation pattern in PET and fMRI is to use regular periods of rest and stimulus. In EEG and MEG studies a single, random event strategy is often used.

Objectives for Block 2

Now that you have completed this block, you should be able to:

1   Define and use, or recognize definitions and applications of, each of the terms printed in **bold** in the text.

2   Identify the main features of neurons, describe their function, and explain how communication is mediated by them. (*Questions 2.5 and 3.1*)

3   Demonstrate an understanding of the functioning of systems or neurons in the brain and spinal cord in processing sensory information and in representing stimulus attributes.   (*Questions 2.4–2.6 and 3.9*)

4   Explain the significance of the membrane in the function of the neuron. (*Question 2.1*)

5   Explain the difference between an action potential and a synaptic potential and the significance of this difference. (*Question 2.2*)

6   Describe the role of receptor cells in nervous system function. (*Question 3.2*)

7   Describe the sequence of events at a synapse. (*Question 2.3*)

8   Explain the role of the synapse in the communication and processing of information. (*Question 3.3*)

9   Predict the movement of ions across the cell membrane in response to concentration and potential gradients, and the sodium-potassium pump. (*Question 3.4*)

10   Explain in terms of membrane potential and ion movements, how an action potential arises, is transmitted and what influences its speed. (*Questions 3.5, 3.6, 3.7 and 3.8*)

11   Recognize key features in functional images of the brain. (*Question 4.1*)

12   Describe the key advantages and disadvantages of the four functional imaging techniques: EEG, MEG, PET and fMRI. (*Questions 4.2 and 4.3*)

Answers to questions

Question 2.1

The electrical property of the neuronal membrane, i.e. the membrane potentials created by its selective permeability, allows these signals to be generated. The nervous system relies on the conduction of electrical signals to perform its role in co-ordinating and controlling the activity of cells in the body.

Question 2.2

The synaptic potential (either excitatory or inhibitory) is a graded potential, the action potential is an all-or-nothing event. The neuron receives thousands of synaptic inputs; the generation of an action potential at the axon hillock depends on the balance of excitatory and inhibitory synaptic potentials arriving at the cell. Once the threshold is reached, an action potential is generated which is conducted unchanged, in some cases over long distances, to other cells. In this way the neuron acts as a computing device whose output is reliably relayed to other excitable cells.

Question 2.3

When an action potential arrives at the axon terminal, neurotransmitter is released and moves across the synaptic gap to the postsynaptic cell where it activates receptor sites and changes the electrical state of the postsynaptic membrane. Its effect can be excitatory or inhibitory.

Question 2.4

The lesion on the right-hand side of the spinal cord in the cervical area will cut through the dorsal-column tracts receiving input not only from the right arm but also from all somatosensory tactile receptors that have fed into the dorsal columns from points below the arms. So tactile sensation from the right-hand side of the body will only remain for areas above the lesioned area.

Question 2.5

A receptive field is the area of sensory surface over which stimulation affects the activity of the neuron under consideration. For the VBN neuron in the touch system, the receptive field is an area of skin. To say that the receptive field has antagonistic sub-regions means that a tactile stimulus in one area of the field has the opposite effect on the neuron compared to tactile stimulation in another area. Lateral (or surround) inhibition gives rise to this antagonistic property.

Question 2.6

Neurons of both kinds are sensitive to tactile stimuli and have receptive fields in the skin. In both cases, tactile information from a population of cells is topographically mapped. The tactile mechanoreceptor has a receptive field defined by the extent of the branching of the sensitive tip of the cell. By contrast, a neuron with its cell body in the VBN has a receptive field that is defined by the number of mechanoreceptors that contribute to it. Stimulation of the mechanoreceptor's receptive field will give an excitatory response whereas the effect of stimulation in the VBN neuron's receptive field may be to excite the VBN cell and increase its background rate of firing, or it may by inhibitory and decrease the cell's spontaneous rate of firing.

Question 3.1

Morse code uses long and short pulses, whilst the neuron uses action potentials which do not differ in length but differ in the frequency (rate) at which they occur for example, 10 pulses per second is a different signal to that of 30 pulses per second.

Question 3.2

Both membrane and sensory receptors are concerned with detecting events. The membrane receptor signals the presence of a particular transmitter to the cell, the sensory receptor signals an event to the nervous system.

As a consequence of the interaction of membrane receptor and transmitter, a synaptic potential is registered in the postsynaptic cell. The excitation of a sensory receptor will also result (by means of the process of transduction) in a changed membrane potential in the receptor cell – the receptor potential.

Question 3.3

(d) is true. That this is the case is discussed in Section 3.3.2.

(a) False. At the chemical synapse there is a small gap between the presynaptic membrane and the postsynaptic membrane. At the electrical synapse, the membranes make direct contact.

(b) False. The greater possibilities afforded by the chemical synapse are described in Section 3.3.2.

(c) False. There is no delay at the electrical synapse whereas there is a delay at the chemical synapse (see Section 3.3.2).

Question 3.4

In response to both concentration and potential gradients, sodium will enter the cell. In response to its concentration gradient, potassium will leave the cell. Ultimately, the sodium concentration will be equal on both sides of the membrane, as will the potassium concentration. The potential gradient will become zero. (Even assuming the sodium pump could keep functioning in a situation where the cellular balance had broken down, it would be unable to work fast enough to maintain any differences across the permeable membrane.)

Question 3.5

In terms of ionic permeability, a small polarization does not trigger an action potential because the outflow of potassium is greater than the inflow of sodium until the voltage-gated sodium channels open when the threshold value is reached.

Question 3.6

(a) A neuronal fibre (axon) is myelinated if it has an insulating coat of myelin. Myelin presents a very high resistance to currents, which means that the membrane current crosses at the gaps between successive myelin sheaths, the nodes of Ranvier. Hence the action potential activity jumps from node to node and in so doing attains a greater speed of conduction than would be the case for an unmyelinated axon of the same diameter.

(b) If a section of axonal membrane is depolarized, then a period of time, known as the absolute refractory period, must elapse before it can be depolarized again. This is a period when it is not possible for the voltage-gated sodium channels to re-open. This sets an upper limit on the rate at which action potentials can be generated and transmitted along an axon.

Question 3.7

(d) is the correct answer, for the reason given in the answer to Question 3.6.

Question 3.8

The correct answer is (b) and (c).

(a) If you thought this statement was true, you might be confusing speed of conduction with whether or not an action potential will arise. Whether or not an action potential has recently been generated can influence whether a second action potential will arise; a refractory period follows an action potential. However, should a second action potential arise, its *speed of conduction* does not depend upon whether another action potential has recently been transmitted.

(b) The diameter of an axon is one factor determining the speed of transmission of an action potential.

(c) The myelin sheath, and the gaps in the sheath (nodes of Ranvier) allow a considerably increased speed of transmission of an action potential compared with an unmyelinated axon of the same diameter.

(d) The action of the sodium-potassium pump is to exchange ions across the membrane at a fairly steady 'background' rate. Its activity does not fluctuate instant by instant and in any case has no effect on the *speed* of conduction of an action potential.

(e) For a given set of axon properties (e.g. diameter, presence or absence of myelination), the action potential travels at a constant speed, irrespective of the length of the axon.

(f) If you thought this statement was true, you might be confusing two things here. The balance of EPSPs and IPSPs will determine whether or not an action potential *arises* in the first place. Once initiated, the action potential will travel at a speed determined by the diameter of the axon and whether or not it is myelinated.

Question 3.9

These neurons integrate incoming stimulation in exactly the same way. The only difference is that they do not generate an action potential. Excitatory postsynaptic potentials (EPSPs) depolarize the neuronal membrane, inhibitory postsynaptic potentials (IPSPs) hyperpolarize the membrane. The effects of all the EPSPs and IPSPs will be temporally and spatially integrated at the synaptic terminals where the neurotransmitter vesicles will be released should depolarization be sufficient to open the voltage-gated calcium channels.

Question 4.1

Firstly, the results reinforce the basic rule that tactile simulation on the right-hand side of the body results in neuronal activity in the left cerebral hemisphere. In more detail, it can be seen that the digits of the hand are represented sequentially from thumb to little finger; that is, they are mapped topographically onto the somatosensory cortex.

Question 4.2

In a concise description the key features could be summarized under the headings: spatial resolution, temporal resolution, safety, and cost.

In constructing the table, it would also be important to make it clear that EEG and MEG are *direct* techniques and PET and fMRI are *indirect* techniques. A possible 'outline' for the table is given below.

The amount of information you would include in a table of this sort would depend on the space available. Thus, for example, under 'spatial resolution' the entries may just be distances with the statement 'not well defined' used for EEG. With more space available you could include 'qualifying statements', for example to indicate that PET and fMRI, in contrast to MEG, provide the *same* spatial resolution regardless of whether or not areas close to the surface or deep within the brain are being imaged.

	Spatial resolution	Temporal resolution	Cost	Safety
Direct Techniques				
EEG				
MEG				
Indirect Techniques				
PET				
fMRI				

Question 4.3

Ideally, the new technique should measure functional activity directly and be sensitive to the concerted activity of relatively small populations of neurons. Alternatively, if this 'ideal' was incompatible with other requirements then it would be necessary to have a detailed understanding of how any measured activity correlated with the actual neuronal activity associated with a given stimulus.

The 'best features' to combine from existing techniques would be:

- uniform spatial resolution throughout the brain (as in PET and fMRI) but at the level achieved by MEG in structures close to the surface of the brain (currently 2 mm);

- temporal resolution in the millisecond regime (as in EEG and MEG) without any effect on spatial resolution;

- the cost, including that for the infrastructure to support the instrument, should be 'reasonable'; although it seems unlikely that it could be as low as

that for basic EEG instrumentation. However, in any discussion of cost it is necessary to weigh benefit against expense and there are no easy answers in this area! Sharing strategies involving the use of the same instrument for both clinical and functional investigations (as in fMRI) is one way to reduce cost, but the ideal is a dedicated functional instrument;

- the risks to any volunteer in a functional imaging experiment should be minimal. This generally applies to all the current techniques. However, the use of radioactive material (as in PET) is not ideal. The volunteer must also be comfortable during the experiment and this is, perhaps, more the case in MEG and EEG studies.

(Whether a new functional imaging technique could be discovered that combines all the 'best' features of the existing techniques remains to be seen. More likely, it seems that development of the existing techniques and their *combined* use in functional investigations will be the way forward.)

Acknowledgements

Grateful acknowledgement is made to the following sources for permission to
reproduce material in this book:

Cover

Nerve cells. Coloured scanning electron micrograph of neurons. Quest/Science
Photo Library.

Block 1

Figures

Figures 1.1, 3.7, 3.8, 3.13: David Roberts, The Open University; *Figure 1.2*:
Researchers from the Child Trauma Academy led by Bruce D. Perry, MD PhD;
Figure 1.9: Courtesy of Bio-Rad Laboratories; *Figure 1.11*: Centre for Brain and
Cognitive Development, Birkbeck, University of London; *Figure 2.17*: © College
of Integrated Chinese Medicine; *Figures 3.4, 3.5a*: SCALA Picture Library;
Figure 3.5b: Courtesy of Web Gallery of Art; *Figure 3.6*: Courtesy of Doreen Mills;
Figure 3.10: Courtesy of Ross Aitken; *Figure 3.12*: M. C. Escher's Waterfall © 2001
Cordon Art B. V. – Baarn – Holland. All rights reserved; *Figure 4.1*: Isshinkai
Foundation; *Figure 4.3*: WHO/TDR/McDougall; *Figure 5.1*: Wellcome Department
of Cognitive Neurology/Science Photo Library; *Figure 5.4*: Mogilner, A. *et al.*,
'Somatosensory cortical plasticity in adult humans', *Proceedings of National
Academy of Sciences*, Copyright (1993) National Academy of Sciences, USA.

Tables

Table 4.1, 4.2: *American Family Physician*.

Block 2

Figures

Figure 2.2: Scanned and edited reproduction copyright Daniel H. Garrison. All
rights reserved; *Figure 2.3*: Science Photo Library; *Figure 2.4*: Purves, D. (ed.)
(2001) 'Examples (A–F) of the rich variety of nerve cell morphologies', 2nd edn,
Neuroscience, Sinauer Associates, Inc; *Figure 2.7*: Courtesy of Dr Anne McKinney,
Brain Research Institute, University of Zurich; *Figure 2.8*: Courtesy of Professor
Vijaya Kumari, University of California, Davis; *Figure 2.13*: Jill Saffrey, The Open
University; *Figure 2.15*: Nancy Kedershaw/UCLA/Science Photo Library; *Figures
2.37, 2.38*: Guyton, A. C. and Hall, J. E. (1996) 'Unit IX, The nervous system: a
general principle', *Textbook of Medical Physiology*, 9th edn, Harcourt Health
Sciences, A Harcourt Company. All rights reserved. *Figures 2.40, 2.41*: Kandel, E.
R. *et al.* (1991) Chapter 26, 'Touch', *Principles of Neural Science*, 3rd edn, The
McGraw-Hill Companies, Inc; *Figure 2.42*: From *Neurological Anatomy in
Relation to Clinical Medicine*, 3rd edn, Alf Brodal, copyright, 1969, 1981 Oxford
University Press, Inc. Used by permission of Oxford University Press, Inc; *Figure
4.1, 4.4, 4.10*: Science Photo Library; *Figure 4.2*: Courtesy of Electrical Geodesics,
Inc; *Figure 4.3*: © SAM Technology, Inc; *Figure 4.5*: Mogilner, A. *et al.* (1993)
'National cortical plasticity in adult humans revealed by magnetoencephalography',
Proceedings of the National Academy of Sciences, Vol. 90, National Academy of
Sciences; *Figure 4.6*: Courtesy of CTF Systems Inc; *Figure 4.7*: Courtesy of

Dr Robert C. Coghill, School of Medicine, Wake Forest University; *Figure 4.9*: Kandel, E. R. *et al.* (2000) Chapter 19, 'Integration of sensory and motor function', *Principles of Neural Science*, 4th edn, The McGraw-Hill Companies, Inc; *Figure 4.11*: Gadian, D. G. (1995) 'Introduction', *NMR and its Applications to Living Systems*, 2nd edn, Oxford University Press; *Figure 4.12, 4.13*: Cohen, M. S. and Bookheimer, S. Y. (1994) 'Localization of brain function using magnetic resonance imaging', *Trends in Neurosciences*, Vol. 17, Elsevier Science; *Figure 4.14*: Courtesy of Dr Krish Singh, Aston University; *Figure 4.15*: Courtesy of Dr Nigel Goddard, Pittsburgh Supercomputing Centre.

Photographs

p. 78: The Nobel Foundation.

p.107: The Montreal Neurological Institute and the Penfield Archive.

Every effort has been made to trace all the copyright owners, but if any has been inadvertently overlooked, the publishers will be pleased to make the necessary arrangements at the first opportunity.

Glossary for Blocks 1 and 2

α-amino acids   Compounds with molecules having an amino group ($-NH_2$) and a carboxyl group ($-CO_2H$) attached to the same carbon atom. The constituents of the naturally occurring group of molecules called proteins. There are 20 different amino acids found in proteins.

absolute refractory period   The period of time after the generation of an action potential when no amount of depolarization can initiate another action potential.

action potential   A momentary and localized change in electrical potential across the membrane of a neuron (or muscle cell) caused by a rapid change in the membrane's permeability to Na^+.

active transport   Transport of a substance across a biological membrane against its concentration gradient. This process requires energy.

adaptation   (1) The change in perception of a sensory experience with time while the stimulus is unchanged. (2) Sensory receptor adjustment to different levels of stimulation which allows systems to operate over a wide dynamic range. *See* sensory adaptation.

additive primary colours   The three colours of light (red, green and blue) that are sufficient to create any colour of the visible spectrum.

afferent   Carrying information towards more central structures.

ageusia   The absence of the sense of taste.

all-or-nothing response   The response of the neuron once the threshold potential is reached, i.e. the firing of the action potential. Below threshold, there is no response.

amplitude   The maximum departure of an oscillating system from its average value.

anosmia   The absence of the sense of smell.

anterior   Below the neck, the direction towards the front. *See also* ventral.

arachidonic acid (AA)   A polyunsaturated fatty acid that can act as an intracellular messenger. It is released from cell membranes by the action of an enzyme which is activated by G-proteins (and by some other stimuli). It acts to stimulate a variety of intracellular signalling pathways and is a precursor of other signalling molecules such as prostaglandins.

association axon   Axon which links two areas of the cerebral cortex.

astrocyte   A type of star-shaped glial cell found in large numbers in the CNS. Astrocytes give structural support to neurons and are thought to be involved in the regulation of their metabolism.

axon hillock   The region of the cell body from which the axon emerges, and where the action potential is usually first generated.

axon   The extension of a neuron that by virtue of its excitable membrane, conducts action potentials away from the cell body.

axon terminal   Small terminal expansion of the axon at the synapse where neurotransmitter molecules are stored and released.

axoplasm   The intracellular constituents within an axon.

background firing rate   The spontaneous rate of generation of action potentials in a neuron in the absence of stimulation, e.g. the activity observed in retinal ganglion cells when their receptive fields are uniformly illuminated.

blood-brain barrier   A barrier formed by special cells, with tight seals between them, that line the blood vessels of the brain; it regulates the movements of chemicals from the blood to the fluid that bathes the neurons of the brain.

bodily senses   *See* somatic sensory system.

brainstem   The collective name for the midbrain and the pons and medulla of the hindbrain.

Brodmann's areas   The 47 separate zones of the brain differentiated by the German neuroscientist Korbinian Brodmann on the basis of their visually distinctive anatomical appearance.

carriers   Also called transporters, these membrane proteins transfer small specific molecules and ions across membranes. They bind to a solute molecule (or ion) and release it on the other side of the membrane. Carrier-mediated transport can be either passive or active.

caudal   Below the neck, the direction towards the feet; above the neck, towards the back of the brain.

central canal   The tube running down the centre of the spinal cord, filled with cerebrospinal fluid (CSF).

central nervous system (CNS) The brain and spinal cord.

cerebellum The portion of the brain located beneath the occipital and temporal lobes. A component, together with the pons and medulla, of the hindbrain. It is primarily a movement control centre.

cerebral cortex The outer layer of neurons that covers the cerebral hemispheres of mammals and is responsible for sensations, perceptions, learning, voluntary movement, speech and cognition.

cerebral hemispheres The two halves of the main brain mass lying on either side of the sagittal plane above the brainstem and cerebellum.

cerebrospinal fluid (CSF) The fluid produced in the ventricular system, which fills the ventricles and central canal of the spinal cord as well as the subarachnoid space around the brain and spinal cord. It acts both as a cushion for the brain within the skull and as a source of nutrients for it.

channels Membrane proteins that enable transfer of the small specific substances (usually ions) across membranes. Channels provide an aqueous pore in the membrane through which solutes can pass. Channels allow only passive movement of solute.

chemical senses The senses of smell and taste.

chemical synapse A synapse where information is exchanged between cells as a chemical signal in the form of molecules called neurotransmitters.

chemoreceptor A receptor activated by interaction with a molecule.

cochlea The coiled structure of the inner ear that contains the receptor cells for hearing where sound stimuli are converted to electrical signals.

collaterals The axon branches of neurons (e.g. pyramidal cells).

complementary colours Those colours (wavelengths) of light which, when added in equal proportions, produce white (uncoloured) light (e.g. red and cyan, blue and yellow).

conduction velocity The speed at which an action potential travels along an axon.

contralateral On the opposite side of the central plane.

convergent inputs Axons from many neurons which all synapse on a single cell.

coronal plane Any plane that divides the brain vertically into a front section and a rear section.

corpus callosum The thick bundle of axons that forms a bridge between the two cerebral hemispheres; it is composed of axons which connect the corresponding areas of each hemisphere.

cutaneous Of the skin.

cytoskeleton System of long filament-like protein polymers, which confer shape and support to the cell and mediate many types of cellular movement.

dendrite Extension of a neuron that receives many synapses from other neurons; it does not usually conduct action potentials.

dendritic spines Small protrusions on the surface of dendrites which are contacted by, usually, one pre-synaptic terminal.

depolarization A change in membrane potential towards a *less* negative value.

depth cue A specific feature of the two-dimensional image of an object that enables the visual system to interpret the three-dimensional structure of that object.

dermatome The area of skin whose sensory receptors are sensory neurons that lie in one single dorsal root ganglion.

distal Further from the centre or origin.

divergent outputs The outputs of one neuron that form the inputs to a number of other neurons.

dorsal Below the neck, the direction towards the back; above the neck, towards the top of the brain.

dorsal column nuclei The nuclei in the dorsal part of the medulla where the axons of the dorsal columns terminate. The neurons of the dorsal column nuclei relay touch information to the ventrobasal nucleus of the thalamus on the opposite side of the brain. *See* nucleus (1).

dorsal columns The bundles of uncrossed axons that ascend from the dorsal spinal cord to the medulla and transmit information about touch.

dorsal horn The dorsal part of the central grey matter of the spinal cord. It contains neurons that receive inputs from sensory axons.

dorsal root The bundle of sensory axons that enter the dorsal part of the spinal cord.

dorsal root ganglia   A swelling of the dorsal root (see above), just before it enters the spinal cord, that contains the cell bodies of the sensory neurons in the dorsal root.

efferent   Carrying information from the central structures of the brain.

electrical synapse   A synapse where information is passed between cells as an electrical signal.

electroencephalography (EEG)   This is a direct functional imaging technique that detects electrical activity associated with brain function via arrays of electrodes that are attached to the scalp of a volunteer.

endocytosis   A process by which the cell takes in substances or particles by surrounding them with part of the cell membrane, which then becomes detached to form a 'bubble' (vacuole) within the cell. The opposite process is exocytosis. Endocytosis is important in the re-uptake of neurotransmitter molecules into the pre-synaptic cell or glial cells.

endorphins   A group of endogenous peptides that activate opiate receptors, producing a feeling of well-being and tolerance to pain.

enkephalin   An endogenous pentapeptide with the structure H–Tyr-Gly-Gly-Phe-Xaa–OH (where Xaa is one of the two amino acid residues Met or Leu), which activates opiate receptors.

enteroceptor   A receptor that responds to a change in the internal conditions within an animal's body.

exafferent   Stimulation of sensory receptors by changes in the external environment that do not result from one's own movement.

excitatory post-synaptic potential (EPSP)   A change in local potential occurring at the synapse which depolarizes the post-synaptic cell and thus makes an action potential more likely.

exocytosis   The process by which molecules are released from cells. Secreted molecules are stored in membrane-bound vesicles, which fuse with the plasma membrane. The opposite process is endocytosis.

exteroceptor   A receptor that responds to stimuli external to the animal.

extracellular   Outside the cell.

firing   The passage of action potentials.

frequency   The number of complete cycles of a periodic process in one second.

frontal lobe   One of the four lobes of the cerebral cortex situated at the front of the brain. It is associated with motor control and higher mental processes.

functional imaging   One of several techniques such as MEG, EEG, PET and fMRI, which have become increasingly associated with experiments to locate distinct anatomical regions of the brain that perform particular sensory, motor or cognitive functions, and in what order, in response to a carefully controlled stimulus.

functional magnetic resonance imaging (fMRI)   This is an indirect functional imaging technique which, in one version, is able to detect local increases in blood flow in activated areas of the brain and display these as highlighted areas on a conventional MRI scan.

fundamental   The component with the lowest frequency in a complex wave.

G-protein receptor   A receptor molecule that typically spans the cell membrane seven times. When it binds to its ligand (which can be a neurotransmitter or a hormone) intracellular G proteins are activated.

glia/glial cell   Non-neural cells found in the nervous system. They have a range of vital support roles for neurons, which include guiding the connections formed between neurons during brain development, or producing the myelin that acts as an insulator for neuronal axons.

Golgi apparatus (Golgi complex)   The cell organelle that processes and packages proteins into membrane-bound vesicles for delivery to different parts of the cell, or out of the cell.

grey matter   The regions of the central nervous system such as the central region that consist mainly of neuronal cell bodies.

gyrus (pl. **gyri**)   A ridge on the cerebral cortex.

harmonic   A sine wave component of a complex wave, with a frequency that is a whole number multiple of the fundamental frequency.

height-in-the-field   *See* relative height.

horizontal plane   A plane that divides the brain horizontally.

hyperpolarization   A change in the membrane potential to a value *more* negative than the resting value.

hypogeusia   Impaired sense of taste.

hyposmia   Impaired sense of smell.

illumination   A measure of the amount of light falling upon a surface.

illusion   A misperception of physical reality usually caused by misleading interpretations of the signals received by our senses by the misapplication of particular cues.

impossible figures   A type of visual illusion in which two-dimensional images containing conflicting depth cues represent three-dimensional figures that therefore could not exist in reality.

inferior   Above the neck, the direction towards the base of the brain. See also ventral.

inhibitory post-synaptic potential (IPSP)   A change in the membrane potential of a neuron produced by synaptic activity that decreases the overall depolarization of the post-synaptic cell and makes the neuron less likely to generate an action potential.

innervation   The distribution of nerves to an organ.

interneurons   Neurons that form connections between other neurons. Strictly speaking, they are all interneurons except for the first sensory afferent in any pathway and the final motor efferent.

interposition   A depth cue resulting from the obscuring of more distant objects by nearer ones.

intrinsic neurons   Neurons whose axons remain within the area where their cell bodies are located, e.g. in the cerebral cortex.

ionotropic receptor   A receptor molecule that when activated by binding to a ligand forms a channel that spans the membrane.

ipsilateral   On the same side of the body's central plane.

kinesthesis   The sense that provides information about the movement of individual body parts. Also known as dynamic proprioception.

labelled line code   A system of coding information whereby a particular neuron, or pathway of neurons, would be sensitive to and transmit information on a particular quality of stimulus, such as touch.

lateral   Further away from the body's central plane.

lateral geniculate nucleus   The specific thalamic nucleus whose neurons relay visual information to the primary visual cortex.

lateral inhibition   The process whereby, through inhibitory interneurons, it is possible to have antagonistic relationships between two areas of a receptive field and

thus to accentuate locations where there is a stimulus discontinuity.

lesions   Regions of damaged brain tissue.

ligand   A molecule, such as a neurotransmitter, that binds specifically to a receptor to form a receptor-ligand complex.

lightness   The perception corresponding to surface reflectance.

lightness constancy   The capacity of the visual system to interpret surface reflectance consistently despite differences in lighting conditions.

linear perspective   The depth cue that makes use of the appearance of parallel lines converging as they recede into the distance.

longitudinal wave   A wave with the oscillations being along the direction of travel of the wave.

luminance   A measure of the amount of light projected by a surface.

magnetoencephalography (MEG)   This is a direct functional imaging technique that is able to detect, and locate, the very weak magnetic fields associated with the electrical currents caused by neuronal activity.

mechanoreceptor   A sensory receptor cell activated by mechanical forces such as pressure. They are involved in hearing, balance and touch sensations.

medial   Closer to the body's central plane.

medial geniculate nucleus   The specific thalamic nucleus whose neurons relay auditory information to the primary auditory cortex.

medulla   The most inferior part of the brainstem that connects with the spinal cord; dorsally it comprises the dorsal column nuclei (see above). Other medullary neurons help to control breathing and blood circulation.

Meissner's corpuscle   A type of cutaneous sensory receptor cell that responds to light touch and vibration (found in glabrous skin).

membrane potential   Difference in electrical voltage between the inside and outside of a living cell produced by selective permeability of the membrane to ions. A value of -70 mV (inside negative with respect to the outside) is typical for a human neuron.

Merkel's discs   A type of cutaneous sensory receptor cell that responds to light touch and pressure.

metabotropic receptor   A receptor molecule that when activated by binding to a ligand activates a G protein. The G protein opens a transmembrane channel, often indirectly via a second messenger system.

morphology   The form or structure of the body, or some part of it.

myelin   The fatty substance derived from the membranes of specialized glial cells that forms an electrically insulating sheath around some axons in vertebrates, so allowing rapid propagation of the action potential over long distances.

nerves   Bundles of axons within the peripheral nervous system.

neuron   A type of cell in the nervous system specialized to transmit information.

neurotransmitter   A small molecule released at a synapse, that binds to a specific receptor on the post-synaptic membrane, and changes the local potential of the membrane, making it less likely (if inhibitory) or more likely (if excitatory) that an action potential will be generated in the post-synaptic neuron.

nociceptors   Mechanical, thermal or chemical receptors involved in detection of harmful stimuli.

nodes of Ranvier   The gaps between the glial cells that form the myelin sheath surrounding the axons of vertebrates.

noise   A discordant and/or unpleasant sound.

note   A single musical tone with a particular pitch.

nucleus (pl. nuclei)   (1) The largest organelle in the neuron, containing most of the cell's genetic material. (2) A group of cell bodies in the CNS that can be anatomically distinguished and which apparently subserve a particular function.

occipital lobe   One of the four lobes of the cerebral cortex situated at the rear of the brain. It is associated with the sense of vision.

octave   The relationship between two musical tones with one twice the frequency of the other.

oligodendrocyte   The class of glial cells that create the myelin sheath around the myelinated neurons in the CNS.

overtone   A harmonic other than the fundamental.

Pacinian corpuscle   A type of cutaneous receptor cell that responds to heavy pressure and vibration.

parallel processing   The ability of the brain to take a single stimulus event and to analyse several different aspects of it simultaneously.

parasagittal   A plane parallel to the saggital plane.

parietal lobe   One of the four lobes of the cerebral cortex situated at the top of the brain. It is associated with bodily sensations and perceiving spatial relationships.

peptide   Small fragments of proteins containing from two up to about fifty amino acid units.

peptide residue   An amino acid unit in a peptide (or protein) with two hydrogen atoms and one oxygen atom less than the free acid molecule.

percept   Object of perception.

perception   The selection, organization and interpretation of sensory stimuli.

period   The time interval between one peak and the next of a wave when plotted with time along the horizontal axis.

peripheral nervous system (PNS)   Neural tissue lying outside the brain and spinal cord; it includes the axons of sensory and motor neurons connecting the central nervous system with the periphery.

perspective   A sense of three dimensions in a two-dimensional image.

phantom limb pain   The perception of pain localized in an amputated limb.

pheromones   Substances produced by animals that act as chemical signals to communicate with others, usually but not invariably members of the same species.

photoreceptor   A receptor cell activated by and involved in the sensation of vision.

pinna   The external visible part of the outer ear referred to colloquially as 'the ear'.

pitch   The psychological attribute of sound most closely associated with the frequency of the sound.

plasma membrane   Alternative name for the (outer) cell membrane in animal cells.

polyneuropathy   Damage to multiple peripheral nerves, particularly, in the context of this course, those involved in the sense of touch.

positron emission tomography (PET)   An indirect functional imaging technique in which functionally-induced changes in brain metabolism are monitored by the preferential take up of a radioactive isotope that decays by positron emission.

posterior   Below the neck, the direction towards the back. *See also* dorsal.

primary somatosensory cortex   The topographically organized area of the cerebral cortex that receives and processes sensory information from the body's surface.

primary visual cortex   The topographically organized area of the cerebral cortex that receives and processes visual information.

projection fibres   Axons of neurons that carry information from one part of the central nervous system to another part.

proprioception   The sense that provides information about the position and movement of individual body parts. *See also* kinesthesis.

protein   Biological polymers (large molecules made of hundreds or thousands of monomer units), in which the monomers are amino acids, of which there are twenty commonly occurring in proteins. One of the main types of molecules of which living organisms are composed.

proximal   Closer to the centre or origin.

psychophysics   The study of the relationship between physical stimuli and the resulting perception.

pyramidal cell   The principal type of output neuron of the cerebral cortex.

reafferent   Stimulation of sensory receptors that results from changes in our relationship with the external environment, not from changes in the environment itself.

reafference principle   The principle that states we can only respond appropriately to objects and events in our environment if our nervous systems can differentiate between exafferent and reafferent sensory input.

receptive field   That part of the sensory field which, when stimulated, activates the neuron under study, e.g. the small patch of skin from which a single sensory neuron gets its input, or a larger area of skin from which a single cell in the cerebral cortex gets its input through the convergence onto it of neurons in the ascending pathways.

receptor   (1) A sensory cell which responds to a particular kind of stimulus, e.g. a light receptor responds to light. Some receptors, such as proprioceptors, respond to an internal stimulus; others, such as light receptors and touch receptors, respond to an external stimulus. (2) A

membrane-bound protein that binds to a signalling chemical (the ligand) such as a neurotransmitter and, as a consequence of this, alters its activity.

receptor potential   The electrical signal (change in the membrane potential) produced by appropriate stimulation of a sensory cell.

reflectance   The proportion or percentage of the light falling upon a surface which is reflected by that surface.

refractory period   The period of time when the cell is hyperpolarized; this is made up of the absolute and relative refractory periods.

relative height   A depth cue resulting from the position of an object in a picture relative to the horizon.

relative refractory period   The period of recovery after an action potential, during which action potentials can only be produced by stimulation greater than normal.

relative size   A depth cue arising from the relative sizes of objects, animals or people in a picture that are known to have a different relation in reality.

repolarization   The return of the membrane potential to its resting state during an action potential.

resting membrane potential   The membrane potential of a neuron which is at rest (i.e. when it is not being electrically or chemically stimulated).

reticular system   A complex network of neurons in the brainstem (i.e. mid-brain, pons and medulla) that has extensive connections with other brain regions. It causes arousal.

rostral   Below the neck, the direction towards the brain; above the neck, towards the front of the brain.

sagittal plane   The plane that divides the brain into left and right halves.

satellite cell   A type of cell in the peripheral nervous system that helps to protect, nourish and maintain neurons.

Schwann cell   A type of glial cell in the peripheral nervous system that forms a myelin sheath around axons and thereby speeds up the conduction of action potentials.

second messengers   Molecules within the cell that transmit information between different parts of the cell. Some are responsible for opening receptor-gated channels following the binding of transmitter molecules to receptors.

semicircular canals   The organs of balance, located in the inner ear.

sensation   Transduction of stimuli by sensory receptors into electrical signals and their subsequent transmission to the central nervous system.

sensory adaptation   A property of sensory receptors which results in a decrease in action potential firing frequency in an afferent neuron when a constant stimulus is applied to its receptive field. Two types of adaptation are distinguished: in rapidly adapting receptors, firing ceases soon after the onset of a maintained stimulus; in slowly adapting receptors, firing continues throughout the period of stimulation.

sensory modality   A particular sense.

single image random dot stereogram (SIRDS)   A two-dimensional graphic with a hidden three-dimensional image encoded within a random pattern of dots. The acronym SIRDS is sometimes taken to include single image stereograms.

single image stereogram (SIS)   A two-dimensional graphic with a hidden three-dimensional image encoded within a repeating pattern.

size constancy   The perception of an object to be a particular size irrespective of the absolute size of its image on the retina.

sodium pump (sodium-potassium pump/sodium-potassium ATPase pump)   The active mechanism in the membrane of a neuron whereby Na^+ ions are expelled from the inside of the cell and K^+ ions retrieved from the outside.

somatic sensory system   The part of the peripheral nervous system concerned with the bodily or general senses of touch, pain, temperature, proprioception and kinesthesis.

somatosensory system   See somatic sensory system.

sound waveform   The variation of the pressure of a sound wave at a particular point in space plotted against time.

spatial resolution   The resolving power in space and, in general terms, is measured as the distance two objects must be separated in order that they can be separately distinguished. In terms of functional imaging, spatial imaging can be taken to be the smallest distance over which distinct and reliable information relating to local brain activity can be established.

spatial summation   The integration of the depolarizing or hyperpolarizing effects occurring at synapses at different locations on the neuron.

spinal cord   The part of the central nervous system that is located within the column of vertebrae that make up the spine.

stimulus paradigm   This refers to the manner, often either periodic or random single event, in which a stimulus is presented to a volunteer in a functional imaging experiment.

striate cortex   The part of the cortex that receives the primary visual input.

structural imaging techniques   These are techniques, such as CT and MRI, which provide high resolution images of the internal structure of the body and have important clinical applications, for example, in the detection of the presence of abnormalities and tumours.

subjective contour   The perception of edges that do not actually exist, as though they were the outlines of real objects.

subtractive primary colours   The colours of pigments or dyes cyan, magenta and yellow that are sufficient to create any colour of the visible spectrum.

sulcus (pl. sulci)   The furrow between two gyri in the cerebral cortex.

superior   Above the neck, the direction towards the top of the brain. *See also* dorsal.

synapse   The area of close contact between a neuron and another excitable cell (e.g. neuron, muscle or gland) with which it communicates (i.e. the functional connection between the two cells).

synaptic cleft   The gap separating the membrane of the presynaptic neuron and that of the postsynaptic neuron or effector cell.

synaptic delay   The time between the arrival of the action potential at the presynaptic axon terminal and any effect that this brings about in the postsynaptic cell; generally of the order of about 1 ms.

synaptic potential   The change in the membrane potential of an excitable cell produced when transmitter released by the presynaptic terminal binds with receptors in the postsynaptic membrane.

temporal lobe   One of the four lobes of the cerebral cortex situated at the base of the brain. It is associated with the sense of hearing.

temporal resolution   The resolving power in time, and in functional imaging can be taken to be the timescale over which functional images can be reliably measured.

temporal summation   The integration of the effects of incoming signals on the post-synaptic neuron within the dimension of time.

thalamus   The part of the forebrain, formed from a collection of about 30 different nuclei, which relays sensory information to the cerebral cortex.

thermoreceptor   A receptor cell specialized for the sensation of temperature.

threshold   With respect to the initiation of an action potential, the threshold is the value of the membrane potential which will cause the voltage-gated sodium (Na^+) ion channels to open, thereby generating an action potential.

topographic representation   Arranged so that spatial relationships are preserved; in the context of the nervous system arranged so that neighbouring receptors or neurons send their axons to neighbouring neurons in another part of the nervous system.

transducer   Structure that converts one form of energy into another. Sensory receptors convert, for example, light or mechanical energy into electrical energy.

transduction   The process by which a stimulus causes an electrical response in a sensory receptor.

transporter   *See* carrier.

transverse wave   A wave with the oscillations being perpendicular to the direction of travel of the wave.

tympanum   A thin membrane of tissue between the outer and middle ear. Also called the eardrum.

ventral   Below the neck, the direction towards the front; above the neck, towards the base of the brain.

ventricles   There are four ventricles in the brain forming a system of interconnected cavities in the centre of the brain. They are filled with cerebrospinal fluid (CSF) which also fills the central canal of the spinal cord and they are lined by ependymal cells (a class of glial cells).

ventrobasal nucleus (VBN)   The group of thalamic neurons which relays touch information from the contralateral side of the body to the primary somatosensory cortex.

visual cue   A specific feature of a two-dimensional image that provides the brain with a clue used in creating the overall perception of the picture.

voltage-gated ion channel   A channel in the membrane of an excitable cell that allows the passage of ions; it opens when the membrane potential reaches a particular level.

wavelength   The distance between one peak and the next of a wave when plotted with distance along the horizontal axis.

white matter   Areas of the CNS where there is an abundance of myelinated axons giving rise to a whitish appearance in the neural tissue.

Index

Entries and page numbers in **bold type** refer to key words which are printed in **bold** in the text and which are defined in the Glossary.